RED LEAD

Also by Roland Perry

RED LEAD

THE NAVAL CAT WITH NINE LIVES

ROLAND PERRY

ALLEN&UNWIN

SYDNEY·MELBOURNE·AUCKLAND·LONDON

First published in 2020

Copyright © Roland Perry 2020

Allen & Unwin
83 Alexander Street
Crows Nest NSW 2065
Australia
Phone: (61 2) 8425 0100
Email: info@allenandunwin.com
Web: www.allenandunwin.com

 A catalogue record for this book is available from the National Library of Australia

ISBN 978 1 76029 714 5

Internal design by Midland Typesetters, Australia
Set in 13/17 pt Adobe Caslon by Midland Typesetters, Australia
Printed and bound in Australia by Griffin Press, part of Ovato

10 9 8 7 6 5 4 3 2 1

 The paper in this book is FSC® certified. FSC® promotes environmentally responsible, socially beneficial and economically viable management of the world's forests.

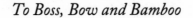

To Boss, Bow and Bamboo

CONTENTS

AUTHOR'S NOTE

This dramatised narrative is based on real events that occurred almost 80 years ago. The characters are also real, but in most cases names have been changed for reasons that will become apparent to the reader. For instance, murder—premeditated and in self-defence—was committed by the Japanese, Koreans, Javanese, and the survivors of HMAS *Perth*.

Red Lead, the cat belonging to HMAS *Perth*'s Captain Hec Waller, existed. HMAS *Perth* I and III honoured Red Lead with decorations on the deck of her paw prints and a silhouette of her.

PART ONE
SHIP OF FATE

I

THE NEW RECRUIT

Hector Waller, the newly appointed captain of the cruiser HMAS *Perth*, could hardly believe his eyes. It was October 1941 and he was about to dine in a restaurant on the Hawkesbury River in New South Wales when a small dark cat splashed by.

'Did you see that?' Waller, 41, said to his companion, Petty Officer Dan Bolt. 'I thought I saw something that looked like a cat bobbing about in the water. I've never seen a swimming cat before.'

'Nor have I,' Bolt said. 'But I read once that the pharaohs had them, *if* they could swim. Noah had one on his ark, as a ratter.'

'There'd have to be two, wouldn't there?' Waller said with a grin.

'Good point, Captain.'

The 35-year-old Bolt excused himself, stripped to his swimming trunks, climbed down the steps from the outside dining deck area and jumped into the river. He came up next to the cat, who dived under when Bolt hovered near it. Bolt swam on for about 100 yards and returned, his perfect over-arm style evident, with elbows high and fingers skimming the water. He stroked his way back with barely a ripple, except for his pounding feet.

The cat reached the steps before him and climbed up onto the restaurant deck, shook itself off and waddled over to Waller.

The young waitress, Anna, hurried over with a towel, and rubbed the cat.

'Sorry about this,' she said.

'Don't be sorry,' Waller said, 'I like cats. What's his name?'

'*She* has no name. Just Puss Three. She has three siblings. They're nearly two months old.'

The cat rubbed herself against Waller's legs. She meowed loudly and looked up at him. Her eyes were gold and large. She settled and sat, staring up. Waller put some meat close to her paws. She sniffed it and nudged it with a paw. It seemed she was more interested in Waller's attention than the food. She meowed when he looked away.

'A real communicator,' Bolt commented as he finished towelling off and took his seat opposite the captain.

Waller leaned down to pat the cat. She sat on her back legs and flicked a paw, claws retracted, at the captain's prominent nose. Everyone laughed.

'Look at that,' Waller said, 'she has an extra thumb on each front paw.'

'She's the most intelligent of the litter,' Anna said. 'Keeps making a noise until you notice.'

'What breed?' Waller asked.

'We're not sure. They were born in Mae Sot, a town on the Burma–Thai border. Dad met a woman there. Her name was Usa, and she was known as "the cat woman of Mae Sot". She had a house full of them, apparently. The woman was happy to give the kittens to me. I love cats!'

'What was your dad doing there?'

'Collecting teak logs from Burma. His business is . . . *was,* transporting the teak for builders here. The war has stopped that.'

'Wonderful eyes,' Waller observed as he blinked at the cat. 'So bright! They really bore into you. Probing rather than intimidating.'

'Green in some light,' Anna said, 'especially at dusk.'

'Green? I hope not,' Waller said. 'The Egyptians were terrified of green-eyed cats.'

'I've never seen a specimen like that,' Bolt said. 'So, an Asian background?'

Anna nodded. They all watched Puss Three weaving around the chair and nudging first Waller's ankles, then Bolt's.

'There is something of the leopard in her, I'd say,' Bolt remarked. 'I've seen cats like that wild in Bengal and Burma, much bigger of course.'

'Dad said that too. But her mother is domesticated. She was called Nuarn and had just delivered a litter. The claim is that Usa interbred her with wild cats in her village.'

'Notice her coat. Black-brown swirls,' Bolt added.

'Not wild at all?' Waller asked.

'Not at all,' Anna said, 'sweetest nature of any cat I've known.'

Waller continued to stare at the cat, and then blinked.

'Why are you doing that?' Bolt asked.

'If you stare at a cat, it triggers a defence mechanism, because you may be a predator. If you blink, it registers you are a friend, not a foe.'

'Huh! I don't think this little miss is scared of anything.'

At the end of the meal, Anna asked Waller, 'Would you like Puss Three?'

'No, no,' Waller said, 'I couldn't . . .'

'She'd be a terrific mouser,' Bolt said with a grin, seeing Waller softening.

'Mouser?' Anna said. 'Try rats. We had plenty before Puss Three and the others arrived. Now all rodents have disappeared.'

'Go on, Captain,' Bolt goaded, 'there'll be plenty of them on the old girl. She can also be used as a "cat-o-nine-tails".'

Waller felt the cat attacking his ankles, claws retracted. Then she began licking Bolt's feet, which had skin joining the toes, like those of a frog.

Anna stopped her, saying, 'She does that when she's bored, or wants attention.'

Bolt picked her up and she began to knead his stomach, pushing her paws into him in a rhythmic fashion.

'She only does that when she really likes someone,' Anna commented, 'it's called making biscuits—a sign of content-ment.' She laughed and added, 'That's two of you on *Perth* she fancies!'

*

A week later, Anna, carrying Puss Three in a small wooden cage, arrived at the gangway of the 190-yard-long, sleek, pale grey cruiser, HMAS *Perth*, which was moored at Sydney's Woolloomooloo wharf. She could hear a band playing *Waltzing Matilda*. Sailors in their distinctive white uniforms were running on the deck and a game of cricket was in play. The smell of fresh paint wafted from the ship's side as four men worked on a darker grey for the starboard side. Anna looked up at the imposing vessel with its dual exhaust funnels, and eight 6-inch guns fitted in four twin turrets. She was in awe of the ship's appearance of invincibility.

Anna approached a friend, Able Seaman Bob Collins, who was just about to board the ship.

'What's this?' Collins said.

'It's for the captain.'

'A bloody cat!'

'All the ships have them. You know that.'

'Yeah, but . . .'

'Just take her to him, Bob. He's expecting her.'

'Gosh. I've only met him once.'

Anna handed him the cage. 'The captain seemed like a nice bloke—good manners, polite,' she said, more of a question than a statement. 'I mean, he'll look after her, won't he?'

'Hardover Hec? He has a huge reputation. Some reckon he's the top naval officer of his generation. He was big in the Med against the Germans and the Italians at Tobruk. He has a DSO . . .'

'I was thinking of his humanity, his compassion.'

'Jeez, I dunno. All the sailors reckon he's tough but a real good bloke.'

Collins waved a hand at about 300 men in civvies lining up at an office on the wharf.

'No one is leaving the *Perth*,' he said, 'they all want to get aboard.'

*

Collins made his way up to the captain's cabin on the bridge and knocked on the door. Waller was seated at the ship's console, sucking on a pipe, when Collins entered.

'Arh, er, Anna . . .' he began, but before he could explain, Waller had taken the cat from the cage.

'You little beauty!' Waller said, putting the animal on the floor. 'I'm told she is a terrific ratter. Will you arrange for a cat litter, milk, food, and have the carpenter make her a small bed—no, a wooden box-couch.'

'Yes, sir, Captain, sir. Arh . . . Anna wanted me to tell you the cat's two months old and has already been spayed. Cats can become pregnant when they're only four months old.'

'Good, good,' Waller said, bending down. 'Can't have any of those dirty old Sydney toms attempting to have a family with you, can we, eh?'

'You don't want to pick her up, sir?'

'No, I'll respect her space for the first few days until she is entirely comfortable with me and the ship. But I can play games with her. Bring a ball of string, a tennis ball, and also tell the carpenters to make her a small hammock too.'

'A hammock?'

'Yes. She's a princess of the Kingdom of Thailand, we think. Besides, cats sleep more than half the day. If she's the rat-catcher I've been told, she'll need plenty of rest.'

Collins did as instructed within two hours, bringing cat food, water, milk, string, a tennis ball, litter box and a cushion. He explained to Waller that the carpenter would bring the box-couch and hammock to his cabin the next day. Collins was surprised to hear Waller say he had already taught the cat to shake hands.

'Where is she?' Collins said.

Waller pointed to the top of a bookcase. The cat was looking down. She meowed when Collins glanced up.

'How the hell—er, how'd the little devil get up that high?'

'Easy. Leapt from my desk.'

'That's gotta be 10 or 12 feet!'

'She seems to love heights.' The captain beckoned her down and placed some cat food in a dish. She hurried down, making expectant noises.

'Watch this,' Waller said. He held his hands together and bent forward. The cat jumped over his hands. Waller had the cat repeat the act, then pushed the food to her.

'Bloody smart, sir!' Collins blurted. 'Sorry, sir.'

'Correct, Able Seaman,' Waller said, and added without rancour, 'but no need to swear. Always attempt to express yourself better on this ship.'

'Yes, sir, Captain, sir.'

Later that evening, Waller slipped into a warm bath, and was dozing when he heard a sudden splash. The cat had slid into the bath and was swimming around, being careful to stay at one end.

'Puss Three!' Waller said with a grin. 'You are amazing!'

Waller made a note to tell Collins to take her to the water for a swim.

2

THE THREAT

HMAS *Perth* underwent a refit and the paint touch-up continued in late November 1941. Twenty seamen worked hard on many of the ship's surfaces. The different shades of grey, allegedly for camouflage, were given an additional red hue in places to give it a less sombre appearance. Waller increasingly let his cat roam the decks, and finally let her out at night.

Early in December, he awoke at 6 a.m., dressed, and walked out of the cabin to find a fresh bunch of intelligence, mainly cables, sitting on the doorstep. Lying a yard away was the gruesome sight of a sizeable headless rat.

'That bloody cat,' he mumbled, 'where is she?'

Then he smiled to himself. She was only doing her job and it was one reason he'd accepted her as a shipmate.

The next two mornings, similar rodent corpses were left for his dawn appreciation. On the third day, she appeared and rubbed her chin and body on Waller's calves. She meowed and kept weaving around him. Waller got down on his haunches and stroked her. He pointed at her latest offering on the doorstep.

'Good work, excellent!' he said in the highest falsetto he could manage, aware that cats were less threatened by a higher voice register, roughly similar to their own vocal sounds. At that moment, Junior Petty Officer James Cook stepped into view.

'Have this cleaned up, will you?' Waller said, resuming his dignified bass voice.

'Of course, Captain. She seems set on impressing you.'

'Yes, and long may she do so, Mr Cook. At this rate we will be free of rat infestation and potential disease, not to mention food contamination.'

Waller found another rodent, this one smaller than the earlier ones and with its head intact, at the steps to the captain's bridge, as if the cat was making certain that he did not miss it.

On her fourth night out, in an attempt to add to the tally of rodent kills, she knocked over a tin of red paint. In the scurry to corner the rat, she left red paw prints all over the deck. The rat was covered in scratches and red marks, which the seaman who found it, again not far from the captain's cabin and the bridge's compass platform, thought at first were blood.

Waller emerged from his cabin at the sound of the ship's bell and moved up to the bridge to do some deep knee bends and press-ups. He noticed the paw prints on the steps up. An officer was busy organising seamen to clean up the paint.

'Your lovely cat knocked over a paint tin,' the officer began.

'I can see that.'

'Afraid she left her prints right along the deck. Red lead is very hard to remove, Captain.'

'Red lead,' Waller mused, 'Red lead . . .'

He rubbed his chin and took time to light his pipe.

'Leave the prints, Lieutenant. They will become a symbol of this grand ship. We need distinctive new signs.' He paused, puffed his pipe and smiled through the smoke. 'Along with a new skipper.'

The lieutenant seemed bemused.

The cat, also up early, was strolling along the long barrel of one of the 6-inch guns. Waller pointed.

'She is a courageous mascot. We'll call her Red Lead.'

'Aye, aye, Captain.'

They both laughed as the cat reached the end of the barrel. She looked down and around. Then she disappeared into it.

*

On 8 December 1941, the ship's cable operator handed the captain several cables that would change the war and bring Australia right into the centre of the Pacific conflict. Japan had attacked Thailand, with its main targets soon to be revealed as Malaya and Singapore. British diplomats were warning that the Thais would put up only token resistance. This was not quite accurate. Thai troops defended for twelve hours on southern beaches before the Thai government declared a ceasefire and that their country was 'open'. In common parlance they were capitulating to the invaders and saying, 'You can do what you like with us. We won't fight you.'

Rogue elements of the Thai Army kept fighting in the north of the country but had little impact and were reduced to guerilla activity, which was contained by the invaders.

Waller called his commanders to the bridge for an emergency conference. Just as they assembled another cable informed him that the Japanese had attacked Pearl Harbor. The US fleet there had been mauled when 353 planes from six Japanese battleships hit the unsuspecting American base for two hours. Eighteen ships were sunk, 188 aircraft were destroyed and 2043 American personnel were killed.

Waller was asked what he thought it meant. He filled his pipe and puffed it alight before answering.

'A few hours ago, I was very worried,' he said, 'now I am just worried. Attacking the Americans means they are almost certain to come into the Pacific in real naval force, at least to begin with.'

The cable intelligence informed that Japanese troopships were sailing from Saigon in French Indochina (southern Vietnam) due to France's capitulation to Germany. A later short cable informed Waller that five Japanese ships had landed on the east coast of Malaya.

'They are coming our way,' Waller told his commanders, 'but they'll have to take Singapore before they think about this sunburnt country.'

All key naval personnel were aware that there was a British force of 75,000 troops, including Australia's 8th Division of 25,000 men, in Singapore.

'Surely we'll defeat them,' a lieutenant proffered.

Waller didn't respond. Instead, he said, 'Our issue will be their navy and when we are called to action.' He paused, drew on his pipe and added, 'That is now a certainty. No more phony war. It's on now, gentlemen, it's on.'

*

Waller and all Allied commanders in the region soon were aware of Japanese intentions. The invaders sent two divisions to scythe through Malaya and head for Singapore. Australia's Prime Minister John Curtin declared Australia was at war with Japan. Unconcerned, the Imperial Japanese Army attacked the Philippines ten hours after hitting Thailand, Malaya and Hawaii. They smashed most of the planes there, including a B-17 bomber force. The US commander Douglas MacArthur had miscalculated and left the country unprepared. The twelve local divisions he had built up since basing himself in Manila in 1933 were overwhelmed by Japanese ground troops, who invaded from north and south of the city.

The armed forces of the Japanese military were ubiquitous and seemingly unstoppable by the evening of 8 December. Waller put his ship on war alert. All leave was cancelled. His 'no panic' attitude was still apparent yet his overall demeanour was more serious. He retired to his cabin where Red Lead greeted him from her small hammock. Waller stroked her neck and back. The cat watched him intently. Waller slipped into bed, still poring over a pile of cables, which made depressing reading. After an hour, he switched off the light. Seconds later, Waller felt Red Lead jump onto the bed. She was purring. She moved onto his chest and began a kneading action on his torso. It was like a light massage. The soothing sound of the purr relaxed the captain for the first time in a day and he was soon snoring.

3

A SHOCK FOR THE
ADMIRALTY

The news didn't get any better the next day despite the Royal Navy's Admiral Phillips reaching Singapore with his fleet. He decided to intercept a second wave of enemy landing ships. He sailed with the battleships the *Prince of Wales*, the *Repulse* and four destroyers in a hunt for the Japanese fleet that had hit Thailand and Malaya.

Waller had met Phillips during World War I, and wondered about his capacities. Whereas Waller had seen much conflict in the current war and knew the value of air cover, he was not surprised to learn the British admiral had disdained such aid. A Japanese submarine, the *I-65*, spotted the British fleet and tailed it, alerting the Japanese air force.

At 11 a.m. on 10 December, nine Japanese planes were sighted at 10,000 feet, flying in single file along the length of the *Repulse*. The enemy attacked. A bomb hit the catapult deck and exploded in a hangar. Fire broke out below decks. Fifteen minutes later, Phillips radioed for Royal Air Force assistance. At 11.20 a.m. the *Prince of Wales* was hit by one bomb and four torpedoes, knocking out the ship's propellers and rudder. An hour later, the RAF air protection had still not arrived. The two ships were in deep trouble, smashed by bombs and torpedoes. The *Prince of Wales* flooded. Its power was cut. It began to sink. Its strong hull allowed it to stay afloat for an hour. Many sailors were saved but not Admiral Phillips or Captain Leach, the ship's commanding officer, who went down with the ship. The trailing four destroyers saved 2081 lives, but 326 men on the two ships were lost.

The RAF planes arrived just as the *Prince of Wales* disappeared below the waterline.

Reading of the depressing news a fortnight later, Waller noted in his diary: 'The Japanese have now disposed of the only Allied Battleship and Battlecruiser in the Pacific Ocean west of Hawaii. Our call up must be near at hand . . .'

Coincidentally or otherwise, at this time Waller summoned Collins to his office.

'I have to account for everything in the outside chance we face an emergency,' Waller told him. 'So, I am sorting the trivial, the seemingly small details, and even the big ones that can be handled now so that every sailor knows his duty.'

'Yes, Captain, sir,' Collins said, perplexed at what his duty would be.

'Should we be in danger of . . . what happened to the *Prince of Wales* and the *Repulse*—'

Collins's shocked expression caused Waller to add, 'I am confident this will not happen, mind, but it is my job to cover every contingency. *Your* job will be to take Red Lead with you.'

Collins looked over at the cat, who was playing with a ball of string. She glanced at the two men at the mention of her name. She left the string and wandered with her languid walk over to them.

'Yes, sir, my honour, sir.'

'No matter what the situation, you will come to the bridge, or my office, find her and take her off the ship. Understood?'

'Understood, sir.'

'Good. Now take her to a beach for exercise.'

'Er, Captain, could I do that tomorrow? There is a very big rat the cooks call "Goeballs" in the kitchen terrorising everyone. It has broken into food supplies, gnawed through ropes, even woodwork . . .'

'Send Red Lead in. She hasn't had a kill on the bridge for a week.'

'That's because she's cleared the top deck, Captain. We all reckon she is the best ratter ever.'

'I'm so pleased we took her on board.'

'We all are, sir. Whenever she wanders the deck or anywhere on the ship, she is friendly and open with everyone. Even the men who hate cats, or are indifferent to them, receive the same attention. One sailor, Able Seaman Nadler, tried to frighten her. She sidestepped him, moved away 5 yards and sat watching him.'

'Oh, really? You let that fellow know that he will be removed from this ship if he does it again when we are docked or at sea.' Waller paused and added with a dark look, 'The latter means walking the plank, remind Nadler.'

'Yes, sir. Will do.'

'Apart from that chap, I think she reminds everyone of home and the things we all miss,' Waller said, letting his commander's guard slip a fraction. 'Her purr is like that of a car engine. It's warm and soothing.'

Collins took Red Lead below to the kitchen area. The cooks laid out food in three corners of the main storage area. Two cooks positioned themselves high on food cartons to watch. Red Lead had been given a saucer of milk. She'd taken a few sips before she was distracted. Goeballs, itself the size of a small cat, appeared only a few yards from Red Lead. She noticed the rat and went on lapping up the milk. Goeballs wandered to a corner and a lump of bully beef. Satisfied with her drink, Red Lead sat licking her lips and whiskers. She observed Goeballs for almost a minute, and then padded off in a different direction.

The cooks thought she, like them, may have considered Goeballs too big to tackle. Red Lead was nowhere in sight. Two minutes later they spotted her climbing on boxes, putting her 2 yards above Goeballs. Red Lead took seconds balancing with her derriere wobbling and tail straight out. Then she pounced, landing hard on Goeballs's back, winding the rodent. Red Lead bit the back of the rat's neck several times as it choked on the beef it had been swallowing.

Goeballs lay motionless, blood and beef oozing from its mouth. Red Lead rolled it over and attempted to carry it off, but it seemed too big to drag. The cooks clapped and cheered, startling Red Lead. They clambered down from the cartons and made a fuss of her. She meowed at the appreciation.

*

Following Pearl Harbor and the sinking of the British battleships, all remaining Allied warships were combined into a single fleet, under the command of a Dutch admiral, in an effort to defend the Dutch East Indies. Waller was disgruntled, even though he had predicted this development.

'I don't know the Dutch command,' he wrote in his diary. 'British or American control would be more acceptable but this means we are operating Empire by Empire rather than in Australia's direct interest. There is no doubt in my mind, and the minds of all my officers, that we should be patrolling Australia's coast primarily as we shall, in all likelihood, be under threat from our invaders to the north . . .'

On 16 December Waller sat in his cabin reading intelligence from other ships about the Japanese attack on Burma from southern Thailand with the aim of capturing the British airfields at Victoria Point and Mergui. The two-pronged plan was to cross the mountains on the Thai–Burma border at Three Pagodas Pass and at Mae Sot, which were about 300 miles apart.

'Mae Sot, my dear Red Lead,' Waller said, looking over his glasses and raising his voice a little at the cat sitting in her hammock cleaning herself. 'That is your hometown! The great Nippon army will be there by now. Thank goodness that Anna's father took you from there. You might now be meowing with a distinctive Japanese accent.'

The cat looked over at Waller blankly for a few seconds and went on washing.

'Yes, I agree,' Waller said, 'I endorse your self-bathing after your rat kills.'

Waller continued reading. A cable from an Australian frigate skipper assessed that the Japanese aimed to push the limited British forces west towards Rangoon, the Burmese capital.

A few days later this assessment was supported by newspaper and other intelligence reports. Apart from striking Burma, taking the Philippines, and conquering the tiny island of Penang off the Malaya coast, the Japanese war machine seized Guam in the Pacific. They had slid into British Borneo and had their sights also on Hong Kong. The Japanese had slaughtered millions of Chinese since invading China in 1937 and it would give them a special delight to take Hong Kong, which was Chinese in population but controlled by the British.

Christmas 1941 was charged with a sense of anticipation. Waller and his officers were keen to take on the enemy but instead spent 25 December in Sydney Harbour on the No. 1 Buoy in Farm Cove. Sailors with homes less than 50 miles from Sydney were allowed to visit their families. Waller and his officers did the traditional thing and served dinner—roast chicken and turkey—to their sailors seated at tables on the deck. The men were also allowed a measure of rum and a glass of beer. Despite the bunting and other decorations, it was hardly a festive occasion with little laughter and much serious talk about Japan's rapid advance throughout Southeast Asia.

There was a bright moment when Red Lead wandered along a gun barrel and drew applause. She had something in her mouth. A dozen sailors yelled her name.

'She's got a mouse!' one called. Cheering erupted. Red Lead dropped the mouse to the barrel and played with it for a minute. The confused little creature slipped off the barrel and fell 30 yards to the water below. Loud applause followed. Red Lead did her 'Now you see me, now you don't' act by slipping inside the barrel. One wag, who'd perhaps had too much rum, climbed onto the gun's turret and manoeuvred the barrel down so that some of the crew could see directly into it. Red Lead duly appeared at the top of the barrel, looking bemused rather than afraid. Sailors moved with cameras to take pictures of the cat in the gun.

Waller turned to surgeon Eric Mortimer.

'Why is she so confident up there? Totally fearless!'

'Notice when she moves along the barrel her tail is straight out. She relies on that for balance,' observed Mortimer.

Waller mused, 'Short of dancing girls, dogs and a few wins at sea, that cat is a sweet boost for morale, mine included.'

They watched as Red Lead climbed out of the barrel with ease and sauntered along it and back to the deck.

4

MISSING

While the sailors enjoyed a low-key celebration there was no holiday for the Japanese forces on Christmas Day as the British capitulated to them in Hong Kong. Australia carried on with the festive season into the 1942 New Year as its 8th Division, one quarter of its army, defended Malaya against the insurgent Japanese streaming through that country on bicycles. The mode of transport tended to make the invaders appear less potent. But this army of about 34,000 were all experienced fighters who had attacked China's east with ruthless intent. They were being met by a poorly led force of 80,000 British combat troops, who nevertheless put up strong resistance here and there, yet not in a consistent, organised manner, nor with the fortitude required.

The Japanese knocked over town after Malayan town and took Kuala Lumpur on 11 January.

Waller did not need messages from the Federal Government to tell him what was brewing in the battles to the north.

Ship-to-ship intelligence about boat and troop movements gave him a grim picture and he deduced by the third week of January that the British were thinking the unthinkable—the abandonment of Singapore, the so-called impregnable fortress. On 31 January, the Allies were forced from the Malayan Peninsula and withdrew in haste to Singapore. The Japanese landed on the island on 8 February.

Frustration built on board *Perth* in the naval version of Nero fiddling while Rome burnt. Waller was given the task of escorting ship convoys along Australia's east coast. It began with taking troopships to New Guinea's Port Moresby, followed by sails to Noumea and Fiji. Waller used the time to carry out manoeuvres as the troopships slugged on their way. He had his crew on alert as he directed zigzag movements as if they were under siege from unseen Japanese submarines. He had depth charges dropped but no enemy subs were forced to the surface, only the odd whale victim.

Perth shuddered with each charge, and caused the frisky Red Lead to retire to the captain's cabin, showing signs of being unnerved for the first time. Reassuring words from Waller seemed to soothe her concerns. She amused crew by sitting on the propeller of the ship's Walrus plane, which would be flung from the deck in a slingshot action if required for reconnaissance work. The crew made jokes about Red Lead being ready to make a quick getaway. She had to be coaxed down by Collins to allow the plane to practise.

Collins held the curious cat as they watched the small plane being slung out over the ocean. At first Red Lead wanted to push away from her human handler. Some soothing words and stroking saw her observe, with wide-eyed wonder, the aircraft as it made a delicate landing in the ship's wake.

The pilot climbed onto a wing and hooked the plane to a crane for winching back on deck. When the dripping flying machine swayed over the deck, spraying water everywhere, Red Lead had seen enough. She struggled free from Collins and scampered for the captain's cabin, perhaps cured forever of the desire to sleep on the plane's propeller.

The number of rodents caught fell in February as Red Lead had successfully prowled all parts of the ship. It would never be rid of rats and mice, yet she had at least frightened them into hiding. The gnawing of ropes dropped away. The infestation of food stores became manageable. The sighting of a rat became a novelty. Even the handful of cat-haters on board had a begrudging respect for the celebrated Red Lead.

*

Meanwhile the Japanese continued their relentless drive through the Pacific and Southeast Asia. They were now in the Dutch East Indies. They sent forces into Borneo and the Celebes, and followed up by grabbing the oil refineries at Palembang in southern Sumatra. Australia's 'Gull Force' Battalion, backing up the Dutch, were defeated on the small island of Ambon. Further east the port of Rabaul had been wrestled from the Australian garrison there, leaving open the opportunity for the Japanese to push into Papua and New Guinea. They began bombing to soften up Allied naval bases at Port Moresby in the south, Batavia (now Jakarta) on Java's west and Surabaya in its east.

Waller noted in his diary: 'Every hour we receive more depressing and worrying intelligence, newspaper and official reports about the invaders. We must wait. We wonder if the authorities have any real plan to stop the carnage and territorial acquisitions. I and my entire crew await a directive to move to engage. I fear at this rate it may be too late . . .'

At last, action seemed imminent when no less than the British and American naval chiefs ordered Waller to sail to Melbourne. Crew members with family in the city were given daylight hours leave and there was excitement for relatives and friends at Port Melbourne when *Perth* sailed in.

As sailors filed down the gangway on a hot day, Collins had to mind Red Lead. He searched the boat for an hour and was assured by sailors they had not seen her. Waller had let her out of his cabin in the morning and Collins was nervous when he knocked on the captain's cabin at 8 a.m.

'She may have slipped off the ship when the Victorians went on leave, Captain.'

'Well, you had better scour the docks,' Waller said, 'she can't have gone far. Take three men with you. It's not likely that she has run away. We are her family, Collins.'

Collins followed orders with three ordinary seamen, who were happy to assist, especially as they could spend time drinking at the Crown and Arms pub in walking distance from the ship. They waited at the gangway, asking all those coming back on board if they'd seen Red Lead. As night fell, Collins told the three helpers to go on board.

Only one very drunk sailor, Horace Murphy, claimed to have seen her.

'Oh, yeah, yeah, I saw the little minx,' he said, slurring his words and hanging onto the railing at the foot of the gangway.

'When?'

'When, when . . . when,' Murphy said, blinking and scratching his head. 'Now that's a very good question.'

'Morning, afternoon?'

'Good morning to you too, sir!'

'I meant, did you see the cat in the morning or afternoon.' Murphy pointed at Collins's chest.

'Had to be morning, mate. Me, I was at the pub as soon as it opened at 9 a.m.' He chortled and added, 'But Red Lead wasn't there. Doesn't drink, I understand.'

'Which direction did she go?'

Murphy waved his arms in several directions.

'God, bugger me dead!' he said with a laugh. 'I dunno. She dashed past me.'

He turned and staggered up the gangway, adding: 'Sorry, mate, I'd help you look for her but I'm elephants, totally elephants! You can always pray for the pussy.' Murphy laughed hard, recovered and added, 'We always do that on leave.'

Collins was not amused. He began to fret that the cat was gone. He felt he had let the captain and the entire ship down. He slumped to the ground at the foot of the gangway, barely acknowledging late-returning sailors.

At 10 p.m. a whistle was blown that signalled the gangway would be withdrawn. Just as he stepped onto it, he heard a meow and looked around. It was Red Lead. She was dirty and wet. He picked her up.

'Thank the Lord!' he said. 'Where have you been, you naughty girl?'

The cat purred. She showed no signs of stress or even a fight. Collins couldn't bring himself to scold her, knowing how independent she was. He took her to his own cabin to clean her up but Red Lead escaped and scampered for the bridge.

5

BLACK FRIDAY DIPLOMACY

Waller was informed he should prepare to join the combined American, British, Dutch and Australian (ABDA) naval forces, whose supreme commander, as dictated by British Prime Minister Winston Churchill, would be General Archibald Wavell. This veteran of the Boer War, World War I, and old boy of Winchester and Sandhurst, did nothing to inspire hope or confidence. He had callously and unnecessarily reported unfairly on the efforts of the best general of the Middle East war in 1917, Australian Sir Harry Chauvel. In World War II, Wavell, also at Churchill's direction, had presided over the disastrous campaigns for the British and Anzacs in Greece and Crete.

Waller geared his ship for certain engagement in the knowledge that an Australian ship's captain would have little or no say in ABDA planning. He sailed *Perth* along Australia's south coast to Fremantle, with the expectation it would be moved north through the Indian Ocean to Batavia where it was supposed to join HMAS *Hobart*. This would put *Perth* right in the middle of the advance by Japanese naval, air and land forces.

Waller received a cable from his good friend Rear Admiral John Crace, the officer commanding the Australian naval squadron.

> I want you to know, Hec, that I utterly disagree with the NB [Naval Board] in pushing you up to ABDA. I want our Government to over-ride the decision, although I fear Canberra will not stand up against London [where the directive had come from] in this instance. You know as well as I, as good a fighting Commander as you are, your one grand ship will not make a difference around Java in dealing with the enemy onslaught. We need you in the ANZAC region for trade protection and for dealing with a Japanese landing force in the islands [to Australia's north]. If you are prevented from doing this, then I concede that our entire cruiser force should join ABDA. I am writing to the out-of-touch NB and our Government to this effect, pointing out that if our [naval] operations are broken up like this then the Japanese will have a lovely time in picking off our ships here and there . . .

Crace's pragmatic approach, from an Australian point of view, was consumed by immediate events and not adhered to.

*

After a false start up the Western Australian coast the decision was made to sail on Friday, 13 February with a convoy of tankers to the port of Oosthaven (now Indonesian Panjang) in southern Sumatra. But a delegation of six sailors, an unofficial union of sorts, met Waller on the bridge. Also in attendance as an observer was Lieutenant-Commander Louis Glenn.

A nervous ordinary seaman, Harry Smithers, a very tall man with a high-pitched nasal accent, read from a prepared script, while a relaxed Waller sat on his captain's swivel chair and patiently puffed at his pipe.

'We, the under-signed, as a representative of the ship's crew, do not wish to sail on Black Friday the Thirteenth.' Smithers paused, sniffed and rubbed his face before adding, 'This along with other sailors' beliefs—'

'Superstitions,' Waller interrupted pleasantly enough.

'Yes . . . um, that too,' Smithers replied and stumbled on, 'this with other sailors' beliefs—'

'What might they be?' Waller asked, his voice a fraction more assertive.

'Well, we believe there are now two pastors on board . . .'

'Yes, our padre, Ron Bevington, and now Reverend Keith Mathieson, a Methodist from Victoria. He is coming to Batavia with us before transferring to another ship.'

'Two men of God on the one boat is a very bad omen, Captain.'

'Why?'

'Well it . . . means . . .'

'What, Mr Smithers?'

'The men think it indicates disaster could, er, *would* be inevitable.'

'I'm not even going to acknowledge such an old wives' tale. Perhaps I should say, "old sailors'" tale. Go on.'

Smithers was sweating. He paused and said, 'There is also the matter of your cat, sir.'

Waller's patience seemed to have left him. He took his pipe from his mouth.

'I was led to believe,' he said, 'no, I have observed Red Lead is a most popular addition to the crew.'

'Yes, we all think he is the best ratter we've seen at sea, but he is *black*, Captain.'

'Two corrections,' Waller said, standing. 'Red Lead is a she, like your mother, Smithers. And second, she is not black. Wait a minute.' The captain disappeared into his cabin, found Red Lead asleep in the hammock and took her to the bridge.

'Unless you are colourblind, Able Seaman,' Waller said, holding the cat close to Smithers, 'you will notice that her fur is dark brown; swirls of dark brown.'

Red Lead enjoyed the attention and began purring as Waller parted her fur and added, 'You will further note that her hair roots are in fact yellow.'

Smithers was embarrassed in front of his fellow complainers.

'I see, Captain, I had not been close up to him—*her*.'

'Even if she were black, she would not be leaving this ship, not on a Black Friday nor, in fact, any day of the week.'

This was the Hardover Hec they had all heard about but never seen.

'This black cat business goes back to medieval times in Europe, including England. Then witches, or people designated as witches, were burnt at the stake. Pope Gregory IX kicked it off in the thirteenth century. After that black cats were hunted down in Europe, and thrown off cliffs. We live in modern times, Seaman Smithers, where such childish superstitions are things of the past.'

Waller placed Red Lead on the floor and paused to light his pipe again. The cat wandered near the delegation of sailors and sat looking up at them, almost as if she wanted an apology for daring to question her importance. Smithers seemed nervous that the cat might walk across in front of him. He walked a few yards away. Red Lead watched him, as if fascinated.

'I'll tell you what I am prepared to do,' Waller said, ignoring Smithers and addressing the others in the delegation. 'I am prepared to sail at thirty minutes past midnight, which makes our departure time on 14 February. Happy with that?'

'Yes, yes, Captain,' the others mumbled.

'Good, because if you indicated you were not agreeable, you would all be removed from my ship, immediately. Now please leave the bridge and get back to work.'

They filed away. Waller turned to Glenn.

'Never thought I'd see mutiny over Black Friday, a cat and a couple of harmless god-botherers,' he said, as his relaxed manner returned. 'We should put Red Lead in front of Smithers at midnight, just before we sail.'

'Why, Captain?'

'Meeting a black cat at midnight is to encounter Satan in the flesh,' Waller said with a mischievous grin.

'You were very fair, Captain,' Glenn said, 'even to give them a hearing. It would never happen in the British Navy.'

'Oh, but there is precedent in *our* armed forces,' Waller said. 'General Monash once met a delegation from one battalion in each brigade that the British wished to retire from the war. The delegation told Monash that if those battalions were taken out, the entire First AIF would strike.'

'What did Monash do?'

'He did what I just did by changing the date of leaving. He suggested to the British High Command that those battalions should be retired *after* his army had done its job. The High Command—namely Douglas Haig—agreed. Monash thus kept his complete complement of soldiers for his mighty push to end the Great War.'

Waller picked up Red Lead, who purred. He stroked her and added,

'We are not going to have Monash's impact, but *Perth* will do her bit in this war also by employing some common sense.'

6

FORTRESS FALL

Superstitions overcome, *Perth*'s lines were cast off half an hour into 14 February, St Valentine's Day, the same day that the Japanese broke into the British Alexandra Hospital and murdered 250 patients and staff. It far surpassed the infamous St Valentine's Day massacre in Chicago in 1929 when seven gangsters were killed. The severity of this indiscriminate killing of non-combatants in Singapore, at a Red Cross protected area, drove home the dangers to all as the Japanese seeped into the town. It put enormous pressure on the British High Command to capitulate.

Enemy snipers were all over the city picking off civilians, including children. Japanese mortar fire and artillery fire was more penetrating with every hour. On the night of 14 February, all the avenues of escape appeared blocked off. Singapore was at cracking point early on 15 February and the straw that may well have broken the backbone of British resistance was the bombing and strafing of St Andrew's Cathedral.

The British gave in.

In perhaps the worst failure of the British military in 400 years as the dominant power on earth, 75,000 (5000 had been killed) British troops, including the Australian 8th Division, were marched off to Changi prison. The news was flashed by radio to Waller on *Perth* as it sailed on in the Indian Ocean. It didn't stop him on his mission to pick up tankers off Cape Leeuwin, with the old cruiser *Adelaide* for company, and sail on to Sumatra in the Dutch East Indies.

He knew that the Japanese had taken the Palembang refineries, meaning refuelling would become a major issue. Waller was forced back to Fremantle to make sure the *Perth* would have a fuel top-up that would take it to the proposed destination. There he found a confusion of orders from several leaders and commanders. Yet no one had told him he should not return to his mission to reach Java.

*

On Thursday, 19 February *Perth* was making its third attempt to reach the Dutch East Indies when, just before dawn, four Japanese aircraft carriers were arming their aircraft and warming their engines 200 miles north-west of Darwin. The four carriers were supported by two battleships, two heavy cruisers, one light cruiser and nine destroyers.

At 8.45 a.m. the first wave of 188 aircraft was launched to destroy Darwin's major installations, oil storage tanks, and forty-six ships at anchor in the port. They city was flattened, killing hundreds. All the ships were sunk, including the destroyer USS *Peary*, killing 93 American sailors.

Perth was 500 miles away in the Indian Ocean. But even if it had been able to sail to Darwin, it would have been outnumbered and sunk by the Japanese armada and strike aircraft. Instead, Waller sailed on into a most uncertain and dangerous situation with the enemy swarming and destroying all over the region. He was oblivious that on 19 February the Japanese had also invaded Bali.

The Curtin Government did everything to cover up the impact on Darwin, little more than an outpost country town, yet a gateway to Asia, primarily the Dutch East Indies. Curtin did not want the nation to panic, even if many in government were naturally preparing for the worst: Japanese invasion of the mainland.

There was pressure from several quarters now for a vigorous response to Japan spreading its brutal tentacles so far and so fast. The words of defiance were Churchillian to the syllable via the American and British chiefs in Washington DC and London. Wavell was being told 'not to withdraw troops or air forces of any nationality'. At all costs there was to be no surrender, a dictum coming after the collapse of Singapore.

Wavell was left in an invidious position. ABDA's naval force was being beaten up around Java. He had weak and limited air force squadrons at his disposal and was bereft of fighter planes. His ground forces were mainly made up of Indonesian conscripts, who had no love for their Dutch masters. They thought, like the Thais, that it might be better having Asian overlords rather than European, and they fought accordingly. Their attitude was not helped by the fact that Batavia, the port of Tanjung Priok and the naval base at Surabaya in Java's east were being bombed almost hourly.

An expert in military failure, Wavell was wavering. He let Churchill know that the situation was hopeless in Java.

Churchill responded by endorsing the abandonment of Java and the Dutch. He turned his mind to saving Burma, which had to be attempted if India was to remain British. But this was not the Boer War or the Western Front in World War I. The British PM was out of touch, and love, with the far-flung parts of the fast-diminishing empire. He tried to con Curtin into pushing the Australian 7th Division into Burma, but Curtin did not fall for his arguments. Curtin feared that the 7th would go the way of the incarcerated 8th, which would have meant that half the Australian armed force would be unavailable for defending Australia.

Consequently, Churchill let Burma slip too, and Wavell began to clear out his office and plan an escape to India.

*

All this was unknown to Waller as he sailed with his convoy on an already lost cause en route to Java and Sumatra. He sent his ship's plane on a reconnaissance run ahead, and told his officers, 'We shoot first and ask questions afterwards.'

Those closest to him noticed a change in his demeanour. Waller was a pragmatist and a realist. He expressed the belief that he could be sailing into a trap. This was a pessimism that his officers had never seen. They noticed he was withdrawn and spent much time in his cabin. Red Lead, always sensitive to mood, spent more time rubbing up against him than usual. She sensed problems in the captain's snappy manner and disgruntlement. He was preoccupied with the ever-changing ABDA command. Nostalgia seeped into his discussions and he hankered for the days in the Mediterranean, when directives from the

British command were clear and structured. Everything coming from ABDA was confused.

When alone in his cabin, he wrote in his diary and played with Red Lead, who was intent on gaining his attention. It was as if the cat was distracting him and trying to lighten him up, which she did for brief moments. He rolled a ball of string for her and tossed it onto a bookcase, urging the cat to spring six times her height to fetch it. Red Lead obliged and was inexhaustible in the games. Yet when Waller lost interest and went back to his diary or talking to officers, Red Lead would sit in different elevations and watch him. He was aware of her apparent concern and spoke affectionately to her, often enough for the cat to meow and, when he came close, purr.

The problems the captain faced were beginning to take their toll. He knew now that *Perth* was a mere pawn in the big game, something expendable as Curtin and his war cabinet acceded to urgings from the heads of the American armed forces. Australia would not be allowed to pull out, even though the situation around Java was becoming a lost cause.

Waller became aware that those chiefs half a world away from the action could not comprehend the pressure on a captain responsible for the lives of 681 human beings. Nor could the Australian cabinet, whose make-up included no veterans of war.

The gravity of the situation for Waller was made worse late on 19 February when the Japanese bombarded Dili, Timor, from two destroyers off the coast. Then they landed 4000 troops a few miles west of Dili's. About 1000 Japanese soldiers prevented any retreat from the city. Two thousand enemy troops attacked the aerodrome, where the Allied forces, one Australian group of about 130 soldiers and 600 Dutch troops (again, Indonesian conscripts), were camped. After a fight, the Australians destroyed the aerodrome with pre-set mines and escaped the town.

*

Waller was receiving sketchy reports about Darwin and Timor away to his east, but no order to deviate from his original mission. He was using maps to understand the depressing and frightening mosaic, and had an increasing sense that he was navigating into a mass suicide.

On 23 February he was signalled by an ABDA boat that a squadron of ships, possibly destroyers and a submarine, had been spotted off Christmas Island, 267 miles south of Java. Waller changed course to engage them but found the group was American. At 7.30 p.m. *Perth* reached a rugged, large rock known as Java Head, at the southern entrance to the Sunda Strait, which divided Java from Sumatra. It was exciting to view from on board but the older sailors were wary of the waters stirred by strong winds, and which hid unpredictable currents around the myriad islands in the strait. The crew members used binoculars in an attempt to see the mighty volcano island Krakatoa, which had been infamous since 1883 when it erupted violently.

Everyone was on edge, yet there was a normality of activity on board. The plane engine was revved to check it was operational. The cooks created omelettes for all, the smells wafting up from the kitchen. The men on watch did their shifts with little fuss and fewer words in a now tropical heat that would have been described as sensual and even seductive had there not been an anticipation of battle in all minds, if not tonight, soon.

At 6.30 p.m. on 24 February *Perth* arrived off Tanjung Priok, Batavia, (modern-day Jakarta), the Dutch East Indies capital. It was met by an inspection vessel. A Dutch pilot was piped on board and proceeded to guide them through a channel to port through protective minefields.

There was no retreat now. Waller and his crew were in a war zone.

7

SURABAYA DESOLATION

Collins cradled Red Lead as *Perth* moved slowly in the sea lane into Priok Harbour. He stood in sombre silence with a score of sailors looking at the desolation of the port area. The town was on fire and black smoke hung like an unwanted blanket over them. Occasionally a sailor would point at a burning oil refinery or a gutted warehouse and mumble something; or someone would spot a corpse floating in the dark muck of oil. The scene was typical of war and a battle's aftermath, and all the men on the ship were gripped with the reality of what they had entered. A shell of a ship, a burnt-out barge, the odd upturned truck; they all added to an air of despair. Red Lead took it all in. She slapped a paw at a floating cinder a few times, but her attention was rivetted by a dog limping along the shore. Her golden eyes became bigger, as if the sight of a fellow quadruped, injured and perhaps lost, was too much. She wriggled to be free, and Collins stroked her into a calmer state.

The sight of friendly moored ships, including HMAS *Yarra*, already an old hand in this war, soothed muted fears on *Perth*, as did the bigger HMS *Exeter*, which also added a sense of inferiority. This British bull of a ship had 8-inch guns, more powerful armaments and radar aerials. The vision through the dark mist of three battle-hardened and scarred British destroyers, along with five medium-sized cruisers and destroyers, also allayed concerns. If they were to be an ensemble, they would put up a fair fight, it was thought.

There was no one to meet Waller and give instructions, which was not an encouraging sign. In the afternoon three Japanese aircraft zoomed in with the sun behind them, making it hard to distinguish markings as they dropped bombs in the harbour from a safe height. When the red dot on the enemy planes was evident, several ships, including *Perth*, returned fire, a bit late and ineffective. A small merchant ship was upturned; another was splintered; the hull of a third was smashed.

The three enemy craft swooped in lower and more bravely for a third time. They weaved among the warehouses for cover and strafed two large oil tanks, causing a loud explosion that led to a tremor on *Perth*. Another plume of black smoke appeared like an apparition and merged with the large cloud hanging over the harbour. The sharp smell of cordite now dominated.

The raid was over in four minutes. The veterans on *Perth* were jaunty and disdainful of the relative impotence of the attack, having experienced brutal and intense German raids that would last forty minutes. For those young sailors who had never been attacked, it was worrying but they gained comfort from the reaction of the older sailors, who led the way in doing drills that had been instilled into them for months, and even years for some. Those novices who'd performed retaliatory 'work' on the 4-inch guns were exhilarated by the action. The fact that no one had been injured promoted a surreal sense of invincibility, although friendly fire from *Yarra*, parked next to *Perth*, damaged the plane, which would need a full repair session.

Red Lead was far from thrilled. She had no drills to keep her thinking steady and relied on fight or flight. The raid left her bewildered and she hid in a storeroom on a lower deck. Collins found her and returned her to the captain's cabin. Waller made a fuss of her. But she wouldn't eat her beloved mincemeat, or even lap her daily saucer of milk. She leapt onto a bookcase, and scowled down at the world. Waller, busy consulting his commanders, forgot about her.

In the evening, when everything had settled, he summoned Collins.

'Walk her around the deck, will you?' Waller directed. 'She is still shaken by the raid. Show her that everything is back to normal. And remember, she is your responsibility if we are . . . happened to be, say, attacked more intently. That was a very mild event and we must expect more.'

Waller had kept his manner matter-of-fact, as if he were commenting on coming bad weather. He did not want to scare the ordinary seaman. He had seen panic among young crew in previous encounters, and it could begin with rumour and fear rather than an enemy assault.

It was the second time the captain had reminded his cat-minder of his job and it disconcerted Collins. Was he being warned of some coming disaster? He did not have time to reflect on that possibility. Waller announced *Perth* was that afternoon sailing in a convoy 500 miles around Java's long north to Surabaya in its east. Alongside *Perth* was *Exeter* and three Royal Navy destroyers, which further bolstered the confidence of those on *Perth* who had yet to see combat.

Waller was disturbed to learn that Wavell had retreated to India, leaving the British forces to the whims of the Dutch, who were desperate to hang on to Java, their last vestige of empire, when almost all the rest of it had been snaffled by the Nazis in Europe and the Japanese in Southeast Asia. The Dutch admiral left in charge was a war virgin, who had never commanded a ship or been in battle. On top of that, the Dutch Navy had not fought in a major sea engagement for 145 years.

There were rumours, but no direct evidence, of a huge Japanese armada sailing south from Indochina (Vietnam). Further worry was caused by unconfirmed evidence of a second enemy force coming down from the Philippines and heading for Surabaya. Given Japan's relentless drive through the region, such rumours were expected to turn factual.

Waller's diary entries were now sparse. On 25 February, he wrote: 'Engagement now expected any day, any hour.'

*

Collins watched Red Lead walking along the deck railing as the *Perth–Exeter* convoy sailed into Surabaya on 26 February. The cat stopped and sat watching, as if mesmerised by the city's demolition. The Japanese had done their worst to this once gem in the Dutch Empire's tiara—looting, burning and bombing everything that moved, such as a hospital ship, to all things stationary, including the majestic Hotel Oranje, which was now a burnt-out shell. The nearby Modderlust yacht club, a luxury destination for Dutch officers, had been obliterated. The enemy was making a mess of any signs of opulence in this rival empire, now all but vanquished.

Collins gently stroked Red Lead, who was not her ebullient, communicative self. Perhaps it was the intermittent smoke that could catch the throat, or the stench of death coming from the water, but she seemed to sense a forbidding abnormality, not experienced in her short life in Thailand, on the high seas and in Australia.

A group of sailors joined Collins and made a fuss of her, each man cradling her for a moment and passing her on to the next pair of arms. She did not wriggle, or complain but seemed diffident and uninterested in human company. When placed on the deck, she scurried off to find a place of solace and solitude in the ship's bowels, away from the view of desolation in the harbour and on land.

*

At sunset on 26 February, the ships of the ABDA force set sail towards the Sunda Strait. It included *Perth* and *Exeter*, USS *Houston*, two Dutch light cruisers, four smaller American World War I destroyers, and three British ships. *Houston*, in design, was more like a tourist cruise liner than a conventional battleship, and as such was formerly President Franklin Roosevelt's presidential 'yacht'. *Houston*'s rear turret had been bombed by Japanese planes with the loss of 48 sailors only ten days earlier yet it carried 8-inch guns like *Exeter*. As a collective, this force seemed formidable and, to the crew of *Perth*, unbeatable.

The Dutch commander in charge of the entire fleet, Karel Doorman, made clear how desperate the Dutch were to hold onto their last colonial outpost: ships damaged in battle were to be left behind; survivors of sunken ships were not to be rescued. This was not the Australian, British or American way but the Dutch were in charge and their directives held, for the moment. Doorman's decision to depart was hasty and under pressure and dictates from Dutch High Command stationed at Bandung, five hours inland from Batavia. His sailors were exhausted and the ships had not had time refuel adequately.

As the fleet left depressing Surabaya, the mood on board *Perth* lifted. Even Red Lead's spirits grew. She drank her milk and ate her food for the first time. And when she finished her meal, she harassed the busy Waller for more. Even with his closest friends on board, he was careful not to let down his guard and keep the aura of being in charge, to the point where he appeared unusually brusque. But in his cabin alone, in the rare moments he had to relax, he played with the cat, who loved the attention. He ran a bath and let her paddle around, then he dried her off and rolled a ball of string on the floor, which she stalked and jumped on. She purred all the time, enjoying herself. Her tireless enthusiasm helped him over any thoughts of despondency.

8

FIRST BATTLE OF
THE JAVA SEA

The next morning, at dawn on 27 February, the fleet was picked up by a Japanese reconnaissance plane, which directed in a squadron of bombers. They attacked but without conviction when met by anti-aircraft fire. Yet it caused Dutch commander Doorman to have second thoughts about continuing. He decided to refuel back at Surabaya and fight the next day. So, all ships in the convoy returned to the stinking, crushed port, which still glowed with fires under a dark cloud shroud. But not for long.

The Dutch High Command at Bandung gained intelligence about a massive Japanese invasion force. At 2 p.m. Doorman was ordered to turn about and meet the enemy. His fleet had to attack the troopships and sink them. The Japanese responded by splitting into three groups, which spread over a 20-mile sea-front. This was impossible to tackle unless Doorman destroyed them one after another, an effort beyond his current resources. On top of that, he was without air support.

The skies were clear and blue, visibility was good and the seas were flat when the enemy was spotted by the British ship *Electra* in the north-east at 4 p.m. Twelve minutes later it was able to report the sighting of at least one Japanese cruiser and plenty of big destroyers. The information was flashed to Doorman and every ship in his fleet. Nervous tension built; everyone's adrenalin pumped as battle stations were taken up.

This was it. Half of *Perth*'s crew members had never faced combat on the high seas before. The Japanese battleships, heading west, would cross in front of the Allied force, in the hope of protecting their troopships, which were being withdrawn to safer water. The two huge Japanese heavy cruisers, each with ten 8-inch guns and a dozen torpedoes, came into view.

The Japanese opened fire first. Those on *Perth* could see the flashes and bursts of spraying light. The shells flew at them with a scream that chilled. Most landed in the sea, sending water plumes high. Nothing in the first volley hit the Allied ships. Doorman had all his ships in a straight line which put all of them at a distinct disadvantage to the Japanese cutting across them. He directed his Allied fleet to head west, which meant the two opposing forces would soon be running parallel to each other. But he had turned too early. When he called for fire, shells from the 8-inch guns of his heavy cruisers—*Exeter* and *Houston*—fell short of the enemy.

Waller and the other captains with 6-inch guns knew they were well out of range. Waller was furious that Doorman had made such an early sweeping turn that left so many of the Allied ships out of the initial combat.

'I'm a fucking Aunt Sally!' he bellowed. An 'Aunt Sally' was a fairground dummy set up as an easy target for people to throw things at; it could be attacked without being able to fight back. This was Hardover Hec, the tough commander, who wanted so much to prove his skills again in the deadly business of battling at sea while ensuring the survival of himself and his men.

Slowly, surely, over ten minutes, which seemed like an hour to Waller, the parallel lines of combatants drew closer. Waller ordered his officers to calculate the range. The four gun turrets were manipulated so that they would fire on the same target. Below deck the worker bees with the toughest job of all began loading the heavy 100-pound shells and cordite charges into the elevators that would push them to the turrets.

Soon each gun was set. A red light glowed. Waller was informed. He was ready to order 'Open Fire!'

*

The noise everywhere now was ear-splitting. Collins was in a frantic search for Red Lead. He found her scampering around near the ship's Walrus plane 25 yards from the captain's cabin. He had never seen her eyes so wide and petrified. She was ready for flight, but where? She arched her back and hissed at Collins, which he'd never experienced before. She dashed for the nearby aircraft crane, leapt onto it and seemed to be considering a high-wire act on lines joining the foremast to mainmast, about 50 yards. It would have been a precarious balance even for this most nimble of animals.

Collins waved his arms and yelled at the cat.

'Don't you dare!'

Red Lead looked down, hesitated and meowed.

Collins heard the pipping calls to battle stations. He was ready to abandon the cat and return to his work on the main deck. When he turned to go, Red Lead meowed again. It was a long, plaintive cry he'd never heard before. She climbed down the crane at speed and was soon close to Collins. He grabbed her and hurried to the captain's cabin. Collins could feel her tiny heart thumping as he shoved her into the cabin. His number-one job done, he moved to a hose on deck. Collins's role was simple but dangerous. When shells landed, he had to hose them down, hopefully after they had exploded, otherwise Waller might be looking for another cat-minder.

*

Waller, binoculars now a permanent fixture on his nose, called 'Open Fire!' Then he demonstrated why he was regarded so highly. He directed his pilot at the wheel to weave this way and that in the bigger *Houston*'s wake. He was attempting to avoid falling shells while, at the same time, ordering his gunners to open up at a propitious moment.

At 4.45 p.m. Waller practically did a jig on the bridge as *Perth*'s gunners hit a Japanese cruiser, which was soon hidden in smoke cloud and limping out of the battle. Almost at the same time, *Exeter* landed a hit on another cruiser. It remained in sight but was now on a distant flank of the conflict.

The Japanese took the hits as they lined up for a torpedo attack. *Houston* tried to disorganise the enemy with a fierce barrage of its red-dye infused shells. They created pretty but ineffective crimson sprays around the enemy destroyers as they readied their silent underwater killers. Yet perhaps the American ship's flurry had caused panic among the enemy. The torpedoes were fired too early and from too great a distance. They fizzled out short of the ships, with minor eruptions in the water that signalled the end of their runs.

The battle raged on for 62 minutes before the Japanese cruiser *Nachi*, using its 8-inch guns, launched a successful hit on *Exeter*. It took out the British ship's starboard 4-inch gun and a crew of four. It then smashed into a boiler room, killing another ten men and blowing up six of eight boilers. The ship lost all its electric power and no amount of work from electricians could restore it. *Houston* was closing behind *Exeter* and the American captain did all in his power to avoid colliding with the British ship.

Exeter wobbled out of the Allied force and staggered on. Steam from a hole in its starboard side signalled its slow surrender, a pathetic and depressing sight for all the other ships.

Waller didn't see the problem with *Exeter* initially and followed *Houston* to port and away from close engagement with the enemy. Other Allied ships did the same. Then Waller realised *Exeter*'s predicament. He knew the Japanese would move in to sink it. He had his ship accelerate to full speed. Guns blazing, *Perth* passed *Houston*. Waller sent out a white smokescreen that streamed from *Perth*'s generators. This shielded the British ship *Exeter*, which could limp on to a Javanese port. This selfless, courageous action saw enemy cruisers making a concerted effort to take out *Perth*, which they viewed as a foolhardy interloper that threatened to upset their plans. They lined up their torpedoes, this time closer. The silent death missiles streaked towards the Allies, and this time had a strike. Down went the elderly Dutch destroyer *Kortenaer*. It pained Waller that he was not allowed to come to the aid of the crew's survivors, but he and all the Allied ships were under orders to keep fighting and not stop. This inhumane inaction was a shock to the new sailors on *Perth*. They watched Dutch sailors struggling and waving in the water, aware that any second, any moment, this could be them. No one would come to save them from a watery grave.

Doorman's Allied fleet was in disarray. Ships wandered in several directions. Communications broke down, through language and systems differences, and also because of inexperience in such a complex battle. Waller would have been a better choice to lead the convoy, but the three empires— British, Dutch and American—would never allow an Australian to take charge. The Allied chaos was in contrast to the systematic methods of the Japanese who had the advantage of air reconnaissance that could pass data down to ships from their grandstand view in the skies. The enemy knew all Allied boat conditions and movements. They had three planes constantly tracking their own ships' firing. Were they falling short, or on target? Were the torpedoes accurate and making an impact? By contrast, the Allies had no planes. All were damaged and inoperable. It was a telling disadvantage as the battle developed, and made worse by the fact that their only ship with radar, *Exeter*, was struggling at 12 knots towards Surabaya.

The Japanese now hunted in packs, cornering the British destroyer *Electra*. Like wolves on a rabbit, they attacked.

Shells rained down. The weight of the attack had to strike home somewhere and the boiler room was the first to explode. Disabled, the ship went down fighting with its captain waving from the bridge. He took the option to go down with it, while his crew took the directive of 'Every man for himself.' Due to the Dutch decision not to rescue anyone, most of the crew would drown at sea with him.

Night was falling, and Doorman had little choice but to consider calling off the Allied mission, yet he still gave no clear instruction to his fleet. He was ambivalent about making one last attempt to find the Japanese troopships, or retiring. The latter would see him berated and probably fired by his superiors in their safe offices in Bandung. The rest of the Allied captains had to deal with a flurry of confused orders, which made the Dutch commander appear like a drunken sailor. The other ships followed him, not knowing if he had a plan, or if he was pulling out of the encounter. Most of the Allied force's torpedoes were spent.

Without instructions, the American ships headed for Surabaya. Their commanders knew they could blame others for the mission's failure. None of them would be dismissed.

Doorman, fearing an enemy trap in the dark, headed close to Java, but too close to shallows and mines, causing the destroyer HMS *Jupiter* to be hit by a mine. It blew in the starboard side and the engine room was flooded. *Jupiter* struggled on like a wounded animal for several hours but none of the Allied ships were allowed to go to the aid of the British ship or its floundering crew.

The Japanese planes now dropped flares near the Allied vessels, giving the Japanese ships a good view of where their moving targets were. It was another huge advantage in a conflict that had moved from clear light to darkness. Waller wrote in the ship's log that the flares were being dropped whenever and wherever he made a turn. This emphasised to him that the Japanese planes were providing pinpoint intelligence to their ships.

*

As the opposing forces drifted apart in the dark, the battle continued in favour of the Japanese. Only four Allied ships were combat operational, the Dutch *De Ruyter* and *Java*, and *Houston* and *Perth*.

The battered Allied force headed for Surabaya; the Japanese closed in. They continued the torpedo bombardment and their fifth round proved decisive. *Java* was struck and cut in two. It sank inside three minutes. *De Ruyter* took a terrific hit but struggled on a little longer until fire reached a storeroom of flares and rockets. The resultant Catherine wheel of destruction made a spectacular sight as the Dutch ship sank.

Waller came into his own once more, swerving his ship to just avoid the submerged Dutch vessels. Doorman and his second-in-command were not going to risk the indignity of diving overboard with the hapless sailors. They found an empty room and together shot themselves. In effect, they were in control of their destinies, minds and bodies as they went down with the ship.

Doorman would have realised that his reputation was finished before he was. He had led the Allied force bravely, but incompetently. Thousands of sailors were now dead or floating in the ocean as a result.

The only minor consolation was that a small percentage of those in the water were saved when the surviving Allied ships, *Houston* and *Perth*, took risks and disobeyed orders to save hundreds in the water. *Houston* stood guard while *Perth* deployed small boats to round up survivors, all of whom were struggling in the choking oil, burning debris and swirling water.

Japanese air reconnaissance had been the deciding factor in the battle of the Java Sea, which had been a disaster for the Allies.

9

FELINE INTUITION

The entire crew on *Perth* were in a collective state of shock and physical exhaustion when the ship slipped through the night towards Priok, having changed course to avoid the marauding Japanese threat. Everyone's senses had been on alert every second of the battle. The three-hour cacophonous mix of rockets and bombs landing, torpedoes puncturing steel, damaged boiler rooms hissing steam, whining shells, men screaming, sirens blaring and other assorted sounds was enough to damage eardrums, and minds, for life. Every sailor, from the captain on the bridge and Ray Parkin at the pilot's wheel, down to those doing the serious physical work loading shells, was bushed. They had used up their adrenalin well beyond what any training had taught them.

It was bad enough for the old hands, but those new to battle had the most brutal lesson in the insanity of war, especially watching men drown. The *Perth* crew members had survived thanks to the fierce courage and unmatched dexterity of their skipper. Yet it was a defeat in anyone's language and that dampened already numbed spirits even further. No amount of bravado would disavow the deeper feeling that the Japanese Navy was a formidable enemy from which there would be no escape. Not here in unfamiliar waters; perhaps not anywhere. It had the numbers, the canny use of planes and the apparent determination. The enemy were the attackers; the conquerors that would stop at nothing to destroy anyone or anything in their path.

Houston had no 8-inch shells left. *Perth* was bereft of 6-inch shells. The ships' two captains would direct a search at Priok for ammunition.

*

Even before he had accepted a beef sandwich from the indefatigable cook, who had helped in the weapon-loading bays, Collins had checked on Red Lead in the captain's cabin. He found her crouched low on a bookcase.

'It's me, Bob,' Collins whispered at first, thinking the cat might not recognise his dirty, greasy clothes, black face, hair growth on his jaw and red eyes.

Only after much calling and high-pitched cajoling did he hear a feeble meow response, then a stronger one, from her hiding place. There was a look of bewilderment, distrust and, above all, fear in her extended eyes. Collins took her in his arms and onto the deck. She did not wriggle or protest. Instead, she stared at the workers on the deck, who were trying to clear the debris of battle. Some were trying to stabilise the aircraft crane. Others inspected the Walrus plane, which had a shredded wing. Collins kept hold of her as he walked past the 4-inch guns. He spoke to a gunner lying at the foot of the turret of the 6-inch guns.

'You all right, mate?' Collins asked.

'Buggered,' the gunner replied. 'I should be at the gun but it's too hot to handle.' He reached up to pat Red Lead. 'How'd she go? Musta frightened the devil out of her.'

'I think it did,' Collins said with a half-grin. 'She's surprisingly placid. Alert but not crazy. I think she appreciates the quiet.' Collins nodded to the dawn light creeping over the water beyond. 'And it's a new day.'

'Never want another like that,' the gunner said with a grunt, knowing full well it was only the beginning of hostilities.

*

Perth and *Houston* arrived at Priok at noon on 28 February. The docks were near-deserted, and bleaker and more forsaken than before. Upturned ships dotted the harbour. Warehouses continued to smoulder, and smashed oil tanks were still emitting smoke, now a streaky grey and brown.

A few Dutchmen manned the docks. When *Perth*'s men asked for permission to refuel, they were told the limited oil was reserved for Dutch ships. Waller, weary and in no mood to be defied by anyone, stormed down from the bridge and confronted the Dutch.

'Do you see any Dutch ships?' he asked, pointing out to the empty ocean.

'We have a thousand tons left, Captain,' a Dutch sergeant in charge of the docks said. 'They are designated for—'

'There are no Dutch ships. *Houston* and *Perth* are the only Allied boats. We are here to defend Priok.'

The sergeant relented and gave both ships 300 tons each, bringing *Perth* to 475 tons, less than half-full capacity. At the same time a frantic hunt for ammunition was carried out. Some 6-inch shells were discovered but only those for 4-inch guns were found in fair supply, which made both ships' personnel nervous. They felt outgunned before they'd even sailed off.

*

Red Lead took the opportunity and made her run for it. She scurried down the gangway with Collins in hot pursuit. She was soon out of sight down a side street. Collins panted after her and arrived at a small Muslim temple. He spotted her on a high wall. She looked down at him, with interest bordering on curiosity.

'C'mon, please, Red Lead,' Collins implored, 'we all love you on the ship. Please!'

Red Lead meowed an acknowledgement and then sat, cleaning herself and ignoring Collins. After an embarrassing few minutes, in which passers-by looked at him oddly, he trudged off. He turned a corner, and took a peep back. Red Lead had jumped from the wall and was hurrying after him. Collins waited and pounced on her as she rounded the corner. She struggled, and for the first time lashed out with her claws, catching him on a bare forearm. A four-inch line of blood formed.

'You little bitch!' Collins hissed.

He held her tightly and marched back to the ship, shutting her in the captain's cabin. He then cleaned up his scratches, and informed Waller on the bridge that his pet had been retrieved.

'Good, good,' Waller said, hardly looking away from his charts. 'Can't have our mascot jumping ship. Bad for business.'

'I don't think she was doing that, sir. Just curiosity in a new port.'

'Yes, yes, Collins. You know what curiosity did to the cat. Keep a close eye on her.'

*

Houston's skipper, Captain Albert H. Rooks, 50, joined Waller on *Perth*'s bridge for a tactical discussion. The highly decorated, handsome Rooks from Washington State was tired and tense after the last 36 hours. He accepted the order from the Dutch in Bandung that Waller should take overall command of what was left of the Allied fleet.

Waller was apologetic to the American captain, who had become a good, reliable friend in a short time.

'It makes sense,' Rooks said, 'we have no ammunition left, and I take it we are heading for Australia?'

'That would be the smartest move,' Waller said, reaching for his trusty pipe. 'But I don't have much faith in the Dutch command. Particularly Emil Helfrich, who is calling the shots. He's telling us that there are no Japs in the Strait. They claim they've had reconnaissance planes up all day.'

'I have the report. They sighted nothing.'

'I don't trust him. The way he commanded the mission, "Fight to the last ship; don't assist those in the water." He is desperate to please his masters. If the Dutch lose, they forfeit the East Indies.'

'I agree. They'd rather die than do that.'

'You mean, let us die.'

Rooks nodded his agreement.

'What do you propose?' he asked.

'I want to consult with [Australian] Commander John Collins. He's been on Java since the fall of Singapore. I want him to direct us to Australia. If he does, I'm willing to ignore the Dutch command and get out of here, fast. Today even.'

'I'm under your command,' Rooks said, raising his first half-smile for the meeting.

'Then you agree?'

'Most certainly, Hec. If we had the firepower, it would be different. But my ship is just a sailing shell of what it was.'

'We've been a bit luckier, but *Perth* is struggling too.' He paused and added, 'We should hear from Collins within the hour.'

Rooks's face lit up for the first time when he noticed Red Lead, prowling along the top of the bookcase.

'What a beauty!' he said.

'Pride of the ship,' Waller said, 'but the little bugger tried to jump ship this morning.'

Rooks stared at Waller. 'So did our cat! We got him back but I can tell you, Hec, it shook the crew.'

'The men thrive on superstition, a cat doing that . . .'

'It's a terrible omen.'

Waller nodded his agreement. 'Especially after last night.'

There was a silence. Red Lead climbed down and jumped to Waller's desk.

'They are freakishly intuitive,' Waller said, lighting his pipe.

'Please don't say that,' Rooks said, reaching to pat the cat.

'Then again,' Waller added, 'I see it differently. It must have been a terrible shock to her system with the noise and bounce, and general chaos. She gets through the night alive, and she wants to get off the ship when we dock. It's natural self-preservation.'

'But so bad for morale.'

'Still nothing to do with premonition.'

Red Lead jumped on Rooks's lap, purring.

'She sounds like a Chevy engine!'

'Maybe she feels safer with you!'

They both laughed.

'I love cats,' Rooks said. 'Never had a ship without one.'

'She won me over when we first met,' Waller said. 'Most intelligent, empathetic animal I've ever met. She relates and communicates to almost all the crew.'

'I wouldn't go that far with ours, but the boys love having him on board.'

'Talk about morale. Red Lead gives all on board a sense of normal life, with a very big family.'

They were interrupted when Waller was handed a message. It was Commander Collins.

'Damn it!' Waller said and handed the message to Rooks. 'We have to stay and defend the bloody Dutch East Indies!'

Rooks read the whole message.

'We have to make for Tjilatjap.'

Waller pointed to a map. 'That means we must sail west out of here and then south. If we have an inkling of trouble we can keep going south in the Indian Ocean until that big island.'

'Christmas Island?'

61

'No much bigger: Australia.'

Rooks got up to leave, putting Red Lead down. She rubbed herself against the American's lower legs. He opened the cabin door and the cat rushed out.

'Oh, sorry, Hec!'

'Don't worry. She has the run of the ship.'

*

Red Lead scurried down to the bottom deck and headed for the gangway, where sailors were carrying up boxes of liquor, all commandeered from the abandoned warehouses. Collins heard of Red Lead's escape and grabbed a sliver of salmon from the kitchen. He hurried to the top of the gangway, and managed to see her turning left on the dock and sprinting down an alley. He yelled to two men just about to move up. They put down food packages and gave chase, cornering Red Lead in a warehouse. She arched her back and hissed at her pursuers. The men backed off as Collins arrived. Red Lead settled a bit, but her back and fur were still raised. Collins placed the fish on a piece of paper and put it on the ground. He withdrew a few paces and kept enticing her in a gentle falsetto. After a couple of minutes, she approached. Red Lead took the bait. Collins moved forward. He waited until she had consumed all the offering. Then he pounced. He picked her up firmly. She squirmed but seemed more inclined to accept her recapture this time.

Collins carried her up the gangway. Spontaneous applause and whistles broke out from sailors on the deck. Collins bowed and held the cat high. But underneath there was a disquiet, expressed in whispers, over the next few hours and in the mess. There was a feeling that what was left of the Allied force was trapped and they'd never manage to leave the Sunda Strait.

Red Lead's behaviour was a sign.

10

ESCAPE OR DIE

Red Lead broke out again, this time through a slightly ajar window in Waller's cabin. He was so busy preparing to leave Priok and assessing incoming intelligence that he didn't notice her escape. She hid in one of the small rafts that had been salvaged from the dock and were stored in the middle of the main deck a few yards from the gangway.

Hidden under the canvas, she would have observed Collins hurrying down the gangway, followed by three other sailors assigned to retrieve the wayward cat before cast-off at 6 p.m. They had less than an hour.

It was still 28 February—a long day for crew members. They scoured the near dock area, including the Muslim mosque and warehouse she had gone to before.

After forty minutes, Red Lead crept from the raft and moved to the gangway. She crouched low as if stalking a rodent, then stopped. She saw four men coming up towards her. She scampered down another 10 yards, and was confronted by her would-be captors. She looked at the water, 5 yards below.

'Don't even think about it, Red Lead!' Collins called. He was a few yards away. She looked back at him. Collins took a step towards her. Red Lead, ears pinned back and body and tail straight, jumped. She made hardly a splash. Collins and the three sailors scrambled for the dock. They lost sight of her. Then Collins spotted her near a ladder to the dock. He climbed down, nearly slipping into the water himself. Red Lead was swimming about 25 yards away.

'Don't let me go into the drink,' Collins said, his voice calm. 'I'm not coming in for you. Come to me!'

Red Lead seemed intent on making for somewhere else. She ignored him.

'Fuck it!' Collins grumbled. 'I'm not going into that oil and muck!'

As he was fuming, Dan Bolt, the 35-year-old petty officer who had met Red Lead at the lunch on the Hawkesbury with Waller, came over. Seeing the cat, he quickly ascertained the situation. Without a word, he stripped to football shorts, jumped into the water and swam easily to Red Lead.

'He moves like Johnny Weissmuller!' one the sailors said. 'Looks like him too.'

'Who's that?' someone else said.

'He played Tarzan in the movies.'

'Dan was a lifesaver at Point Leo,' another sailor said, as a crowd of *Perth* crew gathered on the dock to rubberneck.

They watched as Bolt swam to Red Lead. He tried to grab her but she resisted his efforts so he gripped her by the loose skin at the back of her neck, which her mother would have done. She did not fight anymore and went limp. Bolt held Red Lead high with one hand, and used his powerful free arm to propel them easily to the ladder. When he climbed up with Red Lead, applause broke out.

'He's a long-distance champion, you know,' one onlooker said. 'Would have been at the 1944 Olympics, but for the war.'

'He may still get there,' another said.

'Fat chance. They've been long cancelled.'

'Only if they're in Tokyo or Berlin, again.'

Bolt handed Red Lead to a grateful Collins, who smiled and shook his head with relief.

'You've saved me from the captain's wrath,' he said to Bolt, who gathered all his clothing. 'Thank you, sir.'

'Forget it. I'd do the same for any animal, although I draw the line at elephants! Besides, I love that cat. Most of the species have warmth and grace but there is something about her courage and confidence—I've never quite seen it in a feline before. Dogs often have it, but not so much cats. She is so important for the ship's morale.' Bolt laughed. 'I also love her because she is a terrific swimmer! She'd get gold at any cat Olympics.'

They heard the pipes and ship's bell, indicating they had only a short time to return to the ship.

On board, Waller reserved a precious moment for his disobedient, yet strong-willed pet, now shut in the captain's bathroom.

'Clap her in irons!' he told his master-at-arms, Jan Kreber.

'What, Captain? How, Captain?'

'Your job, Mr Kreber!'

'Yes, sir!'

Kreber hurried around the ship. He found a large empty kerosene can. He belted some holes in it and returned to the captain's cabin. Waller was giving instructions to Ray Parkin about the route they would take. He waved a hand at Kreber who entered the bathroom and found Red Lead pawing at a dripping tap.

Kreber got hold of her and pushed her into the can. Red Lead struggled, hissed and complained with a high-pitched cry. The master-at-arms left the cabin.

Waller took a moment to approach the imprisoned feline.

'It's for your own good,' he said.

The cat's face and meow indicated disagreement.

The ship's log of 28 February 1942 recorded the cat's escapades.

'Red Lead, ship's cat, endeavoured to desert but was brought back on board, despite protests.'

*

With misgivings about their plight, *Perth* and *Houston* sailed down the channel from Priok. Sailors lined the decks of both ships. They looked in silence at the idyllic palms and banana trees on the sandy shores of Java. Originally such views had conjured ideas of Pacific Island reveries and balmy nights, that they had read about. Now the vision presented a different image. Behind the beautiful façade was a hostility from an enemy whom they did not wish to engage or ever experience.

Everyone on *Perth*, from the captain to the fretting caged cat, was bone-tired after the previous day's experience. But all went on with their routines, inspired by the chance to go to sea and hopefully escape the region. Even Red Lead felt better. Waller had set her free from the kerosene can and she had been fed with milk and sardines purloined from the warehouses in Priok. She ignored Waller for most of the time, and occupied herself with cleaning. Her fur had soaked up some oil and muck from the Priok swim. Waller was so busy with his duties that her coolness didn't bother him. He had expected some reaction of scorn and distrust. Yet he looked around for her more than once. She was not meowing at all. He had always been soothed by her normal communication and purring, especially the crackling, warm utterance from deep inside her.

On Waller's mind was an ominous, unverified report that a big enemy convoy was about 50 miles north-east of Java, and heading towards *Perth*. It had an estimated 50 to 60 transport ships, which would carry, according to educated speculation, around 35,000 troops, protected by plenty of destroyers. Waller felt that they had made the right move, given the sketchy data, by leaving when they did.

Intelligence kept coming in that encouraged his decision, as captain of the fleet, to leave the still simmering, smoking Priok. Keeping his calm, reassured tone, he let his crew know for the first time, officially, that they were heading for the Sunda Strait, and then Tjilatjap on Java's south coast. He told the men about the enemy's convoy, which helped explain his decision to bring *Perth* up to a second degree of readiness. He concluded by telling them he did not expect to encounter Japanese forces.

The message had a mixed reaction through the ship. The crew members had expected, hoped and prayed that he would tell them they were headed for Australia. The gossip and speculation were that Waller was *really* intending to go south into the safe Indian Ocean. According to *Houston* sailors this new destination was far worse than even Priok. They described Tjilatjap as a 'hellhole' and worse.

Although fatigued, Waller was determined not to return to his cabin. At 10 p.m. he went to sleep on the deck with orders to wake him if anything was spotted.

*

Meanwhile the Japanese, unseen in the dark, were beginning to dock their long convoy of transport ships at Banten Bay on Java's coast, about 10 miles north-west of *Perth* and *Houston*. The first ship's troops were being offloaded while the enemy protection force of destroyers was still lurking offshore.

Unaware of the danger, *Perth* and *Houston* were heading for Saint Nicholas Point on the north-western tip of Java, and then into the Sunda Strait. They passed the point at 10.45 p.m.

Waller couldn't sleep. At just after 11 p.m. he returned to the bridge and asked for a mug of viscous cocoa (ky), to which he added a dessertspoon of sugar. As he was savouring it, a ship, 5 miles away and close to Nicholas Point, was sighted and challenged. It did not respond properly to two signals from *Perth*. Instead it made smoke, heading for them. The moonlight soon distinguished it as a Japanese destroyer.

Waller ordered the alarm to be sounded and called for action stations. Crew members who had been sleeping, dozing, or going about their routines, were rudely aroused. A buzz went through *Perth*, including a few choice expletives about them not expecting the enemy.

The forward turret of four guns was called to open fire with its precious few 6-inch shells. Waller worried they had wandered into a trap. He was annoyed he did not have radar, held up by ridiculous paperwork in Sydney, that would have given them fair warning of the enemy destroyers that were soon seen on the horizon. They were sailing between them and the Sunda Strait.

By 11.15 p.m. the enemy destroyers were replying to the opening salvos from *Perth* and *Houston*. The ocean was alive with the sounds and lights of a hideous battle, made ever more frightening by the darkness. The moon now seemed shrouded in smoke and was a hindrance rather than a help.

The Battle of Sunda Strait had begun.

11

THE BATTLE OF
SUNDA STRAIT

The two Allied ships quickly felt under siege as the Japanese destroyers attempted to surround them. The enemy spotlights focused intermittently on *Perth* and *Houston*, now both bombarded by shells cascading through the air and landing with a sizzle and smoke in the sea. The sounds seemed even worse than the earlier battle. Eardrums took a pounding. Some burst. Nerves were frayed, but the sailors found a new level of commitment.

*

Red Lead's manageable world was suddenly in chaos, again. She scrambled for the open porthole window and slunk down to the main deck. The noise and the splintering of the deck as shells hit it caused her to hurry back to Waller's cabin and in through the window. She hid under the captain's bunk, which instinct no doubt told her was the least unsafe refuge.

*

71

Waller was in his element as he demanded a full speed of 26 knots and went into a broadside to starboard that meant all the ship's turrets could fire fully on the lurching, bouncing enemy ships that were slipping close. *Houston* followed in *Perth*'s wake, which presented 400 yards of the two Allied ships firing at the enemy, who had not calibrated the situation as fast as Waller. The Japanese panicked and fired off torpedoes. Waller's weaving parallel to the enemy led to no hits, except on the enemy's own transport about to unload troops in Banten Bay. Seven hundred Japanese on one boat hit by the friendly fire were caught and dragged to the sea floor or pulled by the currents for an inevitable drowning.

So desperate and close was the combat, Waller ordered each gunner unit to take control of their own firing. Rough sequences emerged. The Japanese would use tracer bullets to spotlight the two Allied ships. They would fire. The Allied sailors would see gun flashes, which was the signal to fire back as shells whistled around and hit their ships.

Never predictable, Waller sent *Perth*, with *Houston* in pursuit, into a semi-circle with a radius of about two miles, all guns on both ships spitting shells. Waller pushed port, then starboard, followed by starboard then port moves, all the while anticipating the fall of shells, a most inexact science in the conditions as they followed the semi-circle track.

This unorthodox manoeuvre once more confused the enemy.

Yet even Waller's genius and courage couldn't avoid hits. Just before 11.30 p.m. a shell smashed into the forward funnel. It blew nearby machine-gunners into the air, killing and maiming several sailors. Steam blew in a hissing scream from a pipe. Another shell shredded part of the flag deck.

There were no stretcher-bearers, just mates on hand to take the wounded below to the surgeon's room.

These severe belts caused some sailors to freeze in terror, but not for long as more shells hit and men went down, killed or badly wounded. No one had time to think, only just *do*. The gunners, ankle-deep in shells, had the most challenging and dangerous jobs, if any could be graded in these terrifying moments. They had weapons with which to punch back. And they did, their aching bodies loading up and spinning the wheel to train the guns, somewhere, anywhere they thought the opposite fire was coming from.

Waller remained in control of himself, his crew and the ship. But he could not manage an overwhelming enemy. He made the decision to fire all his eight torpedoes from the mid-deck below the 4-inch guns. Logic told him that there was no use holding off such action. He might open up a path out of the mess, maybe not. But to wait for the enemy destroyers to edge in and live up to their name was not an option for a fighter such as Waller. The enemy would never ease up. They would go in for the kill no matter what. He was captain of the ship because he was Australia's finest. He was not prepared to die wondering.

The *Perth* torpedoes were fired without lining up targets. There were two explosions, indicating hits. But no one on *Perth* could be sure which Japanese vessels were struck. The enemy destroyers became bolder. One charged towards *Perth* with a blinding searchlight on full.

'Destroy that light!' Waller ordered. A gunner obliged.

The two Allied ships were under intense, uncoordinated bombardment by at least ten enemy vessels. Both Allied ships were nearly out of ammunition. *Perth*'s plane, its catapult and crane were struck. They caught fire and crashed into the sea. Seeing this, Waller made an instant decision to escape and head for the strait.

The Japanese were alert to the move. Just as *Perth* and *Houston* were on their new course, a Japanese destroyer released a torpedo a few minutes before midnight. The phosphorescent streak struck *Perth* on the starboard side, killing everyone in the forward engine and boiler rooms. The ship pitched up. Sailors were hurled around like rag dolls as ocean water surged onto the decks. The ship struggled to right itself, leaned to starboard, and lost power.

'That's buggered it!' Waller mumbled. 'Prepare to abandon ship!'

Minutes later, a second torpedo struck further forward and blew up the two front 6-inch gun turrets. *Perth* rocked upward again, now mortally wounded.

'Abandon ship!' Waller ordered, uttering the words that gave captains nightmares through the ages, and that no sailor ever wished to hear. The ship's bugler reached for his instrument, cleared his throat of the grit and thick smoke, and piped the message over the loudspeakers that signalled the death knell of a mighty ship. Whether or not sailors heard it over the din and crashing of shells, the screams of the dying and dismembered, and the crackle of fire, the able-bodied men left knew they were going down. Many were jumping overboard.

Waller issued a flurry of final directives. Despite the extra expletive here and there, his orders were clear, precise and staccato. He told Ray Parkin to leave both engines on half-speed, saying, 'I don't want anyone to go down with the old girl.' Then he added, 'Get Bob Collins to the bridge.'

Collins was mid-deck contemplating whether or not to jump. He hurried to the bridge.

'Take Red Lead,' Waller said, 'make sure she makes it. She's had a rough time.'

Collins opened the cabin door. A big clock, in the shape of a ship's steering wheel, lay broken on the floor. Waller's swivel chair was upturned, tiling and charts had been shaken loose from the walls. Eerily though, only one of five ships' models had fallen from a mantelpiece. The other four were on their sides. The captain's bunk had shifted a yard due to the big gun vibration and the hits from the incoming torpedoes.

'Red Lead?' Collins asked loudly so he could be heard above the incessant din. There was no response.

'Red Lead? C'mon, darling! We gotta go. Captain's orders!'

He scoured the room, including on top of the bookcase, which had been ripped a few inches from the cabin wall. Collins got down on his knees and peered under the bunk. A heavy hit nearby caused him to bump his head on the bottom of the bunk. He cursed. Above the crashing sound he thought he heard a squeak, which may have been a cat noise. Collins lay flat under the bunk. He thought he saw something in a corner.

Then he saw those unmistakable big round yellow eyes, staring. They blinked. She meowed. Collins implored her to come out. Another round of shells struck close. He slithered under the bunk, grabbed her by the loose skin at the back of her neck and pulled her out. He stood and loosened his grip on her neck. She struggled a bit and then went limp as if resigned to her fate. Collins moved to the deck railing and looked back at the bridge as he cradled Red Lead in his lifejacket. He inflated it and tossed his tin helmet overboard. It splashed only a couple of seconds later. The boat was sinking slowly and would soon be below the waterline. Sailors left and right made the leap.

Collins hesitated.

*

The Officer of the Watch, Willie Gay, was about to leave the bridge. He looked back at Waller wearing his maritime lifejacket.

'Coming, sir?'

'Get the hell out of it,' Waller said, touching his hat but not turning around. He was staring down at the water. The captain was not making a move.

'Sir?'

'I'm staying,' Waller said, all the authority drained from his voice. He'd made the decision. The captain was fulfilling the honoured tradition of going down with his ship. He turned to face Gay. 'Get off the bridge!'

*

A third torpedo hit starboard, this time well to the ship's rear, just as Collins, wearing his inflated lifejacket with Red Lead tucked inside, jumped. Collins was blown 30 yards sideways by the strike's blast 120 yards away on the other side of the ship. He had a sensation of floating as he was blown clear of the ship. He landed lightly in the water, still gripping the cat to his side.

The ocean was a swirl. Collins swam to a small, wooden Japanese-style skiff with high sides. He pushed Red Lead into it, but it was far too light to get in himself. He had to dive to avoid being struck by a lifeboat on fire. When he surfaced, the cat and her skiff were not in sight.

Collins called out for the cat but there was no response, or at least, with the cacophony of ear-splitting sounds, he could not hear any meow from Red Lead. Collins turned his mind to his own survival. He began swimming towards what he guessed might be the Java coast, navigating through wood and debris. Others were using breaststroke, struggling, and screaming for help.

*

A fourth torpedo hit *Perth* on the port side at 12.14 p.m. It was the final blow for the badly wounded ship. She listed. Her stern was out of the water. Sailors in the water could see the mainmast sinking slowly, the battle ensign still flying and buffeted by blasts. The *Perth* hit the ocean floor four miles to the north-west of Saint Nicholas Point.

It was 12.25 p.m. on 1 March 1942. There were 681 sailors on board that night and hundreds were sure to be lost. Many of those swimming and barely afloat were fighting for their lives, not against the enemy but the elements.

*

Houston was battling on. Captain Rooks watched the demise of the *Perth* and his heart sank with it. He thought of Waller, whom he respected above all other naval commanders. Would he jump or go down with his beloved old girl? He had no time to dwell on this; no time to reflect. Rooks, like Waller, was no shrinking violet. He turned *Houston* back into the middle of the Japanese destroyers, a move unexpected and startling to the enemy. In fear, they let go of all their 90 remaining torpedoes, which came in waves of six. The hundreds of *Perth* sailors in the water saw the torpedoes' silver streaks passing below them, heading for the lone *Houston*. They missed and careered into two Japanese ships, in 'own goals'.

The attacks from the Japanese destroyers close in and the cruiser further out now zeroed in on *Houston* with increased intensity. The ship was taking terrible punishment. Ten minutes after *Perth*'s demise, *Houston* took a telling strike from a torpedo in the engine room. The explosion killed every man there. *Houston* groaned and ground to a speed of just 15 knots. In desperation, the big gunners started using star shells, which burst in the air and produced light to illuminate Japanese positions. Apart from their capacity to expose, the use of these harmless shells soon became an unofficial surrender semaphore.

Houston was out of ammunition.

Its number two turret was obliterated by a direct shell hit. Fire flashed over the bridge. The fierce heat drove Rooks and everyone from the conning tower. Communications to the rest of the ship were destroyed.

A second torpedo hit forward of the upper deck near the stern.

It was the moment every one of the 1081 American sailors remaining alive knew *Houston* was done. It trembled, lost steerage and stopped.

Rooks kept his voice strong and ordered: 'Abandon ship!'

The bugler did his thing, standing on the bridge and putting his lungs into the instrument for the sound he had practised, but never wished to exercise in battle.

Rooks, on the deck near his cabin, began shaking hands with his key officers. A shell hit a gun mount. A piece of metal breach cannoned into the captain's chest. He went down badly wounded. Someone injected him with morphine. Officers cradled their beloved commander in their arms, where he died.

Like Waller, Rooks went down with his ship, which disappeared at 12.45 p.m., twenty minutes after *Perth*.

The Battle of Sunda Strait was over.

1 2

SINK OR SWIM

Hundreds of sailors from *Perth* and *Houston*, along with Japanese from enemy boats, lay in the water looking up at the remaining vessels. Once the grand men on grander ships, they were now buoys bobbing, some helplessly, in the swirling sea of oil. Around them were scores of small rafts and lifeboats, some busted, others intact. Fire ripped across the ocean, fuelled by oil and loose wooden planks, and parts of the smashed ships. Men called out to each other. Some swore; others made crude, sarcastic jokes. This was the Aussie way of showing bravado or avoiding a hideous fear, the fear that they were all doomed.

Ships in the black night, made darker by the obscuring of the otherwise bright moon, bore down on the stranded survivors at a speed suggesting they didn't care if men were run over. Then the sea was lit up by searchlights undulating over the uncoordinated human fish; some on rickety lifeboats and rafts, others gripping onto planks, tiny balsa wood squares and the solid little wooden boats similar to the one that had spirited Red Lead away. Oddly, those relying on little craft as swimming aids to their kicking legs were travelling more adroitly than the lifeboats, some of which carried twice as many men as they normally would. The currents were crisscrossing, some into the nearby island coasts, and that of Java about 11 miles away.

A Japanese destroyer, looking like a giant, galloping department store, bore down on the swimmers, who expected any moment to be drilled with machine-gun bullets. The destroyer stopped, its engines winding down. Immaculately white-suited Japanese sailors looked down from the deck. A few had binoculars.

A swimmer begged for help and was quickly abused by other Australians, who, it seemed, would rather drown in the suffocating oil than plead for assistance from the enemy.

Then a surprise. A Japanese officer with a loudhailer said in a well-modulated tone, probably from being stationed in Australia or the UK in the 1930s, 'Who are you? Which country?'

'Australians!' a *Perth* sailor yelled back. 'And bloody proud of it!'

'We bloody good boys now, eh, Aussie?'

'Go fuck yourself,' a second Australian said, rather than yelled.

'Couldn't. His Jap dick would be too small,' a third said, loudly enough to bring guffaws from those within hearing distance.

Japanese sailors could be seen manning machine guns. The Australians and Americans in the water wondered if they were going to be murdered. Spotlights roamed over the bobbing heads and waving hands, and the survivors realised the Japanese were only searching for their own men over-board. 'The filthy fuckers are looking for their own fuckers!' a disgruntled sailor, big of voice and small of thoughtful alliteration, yelled.

After another fifteen minutes, to the Allied men's surprise and relief, the destroyer's engine kicked to life and the ship was away, before stopping again a few hundred yards further on.

Other Japanese destroyers stopped and took more than a hundred Allied sailors out of the water. To their great shock they were treated humanely. The captured men were ordered to remove their dirty, oil-soaked garments and were given kerosene and cotton to clean themselves up. They were issued with G-string underwear, and fed with hard biscuits. Even cigarettes were passed around.

Salvation, it seemed, depended on the whim of the Japanese captain on any given ship, whether destroyer or troop carrier, now ploughing by to Javanese ports and unhindered by Allied fire.

Still in the water, hundreds of Allied sailors spread over 2 miles were struggling on, swimming or clinging to any small craft or debris they could find. Many who were injured, exhausted or not capable swimmers were drowning.

There were scores of enemy sailors doing the same, but everyone was intent on survival rather than futile fighting in the swirling oil-riven water. Spot fires on small craft and drift-wood made swimming in any direction hazardous.

Anyone thinking about making it to shore had first to negotiate the debris. If any sailors were strong and lucky enough to clear the smashed ships, they might encounter sharks. They were close to shore but keeping their distance, for the moment, from the detritus of war and the deadly hot choking oil.

PART TWO
SURVIVORS

13

THE SWIMMER

After jumping ship, Dan Bolt shed his inflatable life-jacket and his clothes except for his black football shorts, an undershirt and light deck shoes. He spent the next two hours in the water, helping other sailors to life rafts, small boats and floating planks before fatigue set in. He had to tread water for half an hour before considering his alternatives. There were godforsaken small rock and volcanic islands within a few miles, with the infamous, never extinct volcano Krakatoa in the distance. He had heard others on rafts saying they were heading there. In the end, he considered he'd have a better chance of living if he swam to Java, an estimated 10 miles.

Bolt thrived on swimming races of 440, 880, 1500 and 5000 yards. He had exceptional lung capacity and an outsized heart, which doctors had told him was as big as a horse's and lying on its side. He had another extraordinary physical feature, or abnormality. His webbed toes on each foot gave him exceptional kicking power, as if Bolt had a genetic throwback from an amphibian ancestor. He could hold his breath underwater for five minutes, which put him in the class of Harry Houdini, the great Hungarian–American escapologist.

Whatever the analysis, he loved the water. Before he joined the navy, and whenever he was on leave, Bolt swam every day near his Brighton beach, Melbourne, home, even in freezing winter weather. He had a powerboat; he sailed in yachting competitions with the Sandringham Club; and every second weekend in summer he rode a motorbike to Point Leo surf beach to volunteer his time as a lifesaver

Bolt was short at 5 feet 6 inches, but he had 16-inch biceps, never having pumped iron in a gymnasium or done any special labouring. He had won every distance swimming race he had ever competed in; the longer the better. His last big win was in a 5000-yard event in the Yarra River, Melbourne, in 1939, just before he gave up his veterinary studies to join the navy. He had yearned since a little boy to be on boats and in the navy, far more than in a vet clinic. It was his dream. That it coincided with war was incidental. The navy was where Bolt saw his future, his life.

Rough ocean conditions never made him fearful. They were a challenge. The bigger the wave when boating in Port Phillip Bay, the better. He loved the battle against the elements. In the decade he'd spent as a lifesaver at Point Leo, he had saved several hundred people from drowning, and on not one occasion did he feel he would die because of a drunken fool, or a manic individual. This certainty was mainly due to his physical strength. Bolt's most outstanding and heroic act or acts as a lifesaver occurred not at Point

Leo, but at a Port Phillip Bay beach at Dromana. He and his fiancée were enjoying a day trip when he was on leave in the summer of 1940. On the beach was a group of eleven mentally and physically handicapped people, who could not swim. A nurse led them out to a sandbar, to which they could walk and wade. The weather changed and a storm began brewing. A tide came in fast and trapped the group on the bar about 50 yards from the shore. The nurse and members of the group began screaming for help. Bolt dashed into the water. One by one he started swimming the stranded individuals to shore. After he managed to take six people to the beach, onlookers began screaming: 'Shark! Shark!'

A 9-foot shark was circling in the deepened water around the sandbar. Bolt ignored pleas from his fiancée not to go on.

'It's a grey nurse,' he said, breathing hard as he dashed into the swirling water. 'They don't take humans.'

That didn't calm onlookers, his fiancée or those left on the ever-shrinking sandbar. Bolt carried on as he had most of his adult life in more dangerous surf beaches and got everyone, including the traumatised nurse, to safety.

After that super-human effort, he lay on the sand like a beached whale, recovering as the bar disappeared and the shark swam over it.

*

In his biggest water challenge since then, Bolt paced himself in the Sunda Strait, which was variously turbulent and swirling, more from passing ships than any other factor now the furious battle was long over. The currents were treacherous. If you fought them, as he could hear men in the dark doing, the eventual tiredness would pull you under. If you went with them limply, you could be dragged out to sea and become shark fodder, or simply give up and sink. Now Bolt used all his Point Leo surf beach experience of rips, which could at times defeat even the strongest swimmers. It was a matter of 20 yards in one direction to be hauled back 10 yards, with the occasional bonus of a 50-yard swim. He mainly did the overarm crawl, but added backstroke and, the least taxing of all, breaststroke.

He was covered in stinking black oil and doing the breaststroke allowed him to see and avoid oil clogging up his eyelids. It also helped him to see how close he was to land. He could see ship lights at a port. Lighthouse beams now and then swept the ocean. Bolt did not wish to be pushed into Japanese territory on Java, but he was at the mercy of the currents to an extent. It would be anyone's guess where he might make shore.

As the hours ticked by, he began to succumb to fatigue, like any mortal, despite his special attributes. The thin fingers of dawn spreading over the ocean inspired him to kick on. He had managed to defeat the night, currents and any mental demons that seeped into his mind.

The dawn of a new day was a psychological lift.

After about seven hours in the water, he realised he would have to get ashore where he could, even if it meant capture. He struggled to keep clear of any port and rode a surging current that dumped him within 20 yards of a sandy beach.

At first, he could not stand. He stumbled and fell to his knees several times before crawling onto sand. He dragged his body up the beach and slumped onto his back. Bolt believed that this swim was the greatest physical challenge he'd ever overcome. His heart was thumping and his lungs heaving after seven hours' exertion.

Bolt fell into a deep sleep for two hours. He awoke to the sounds of cries for help. His lips were parched. The sun was already beginning to burn his skin. He sat up. The reality of the night's horrific events flooded his mind. He got to his feet and peered out to sea. He could see other survivors being swept along the coast, from about 1000 yards out to several miles. Some had rafts but the currents would not allow them to be manoeuvred into shore.

Then he noticed a man, covered in black oil, 200 yards from shore, waving his hands and in distress. Instinct overrode Bolt's near-cramped legs and he hobbled down to the water. It was as if he were back at Point Leo in his one-piece swimsuit and cap tied under his chin. He didn't hesitate. He dived into the foaming surf and swam hard to the man. He looked up 30 yards away. The man's face was black. Bolt heard the plaintive cries for aid. Was it English? He swam closer. Bolt noticed the man was in a sailor's suit.

It was not Australian or American or Dutch.

When he was just a few feet away, the man held a knife high and screamed in anger. He was Japanese. He swiped at Bolt who ducked underwater. He swam around behind the Japanese sailor, and gripped him with powerful arms, locking him in a half-Nelson hold. He jerked the man's neck and head forward, and pulled him under. The enemy sailor let go of the knife in a desperate effort to free himself from the hard lock. Bolt dragged him down 2 yards to the ocean floor, and squeezed him until he struggled no more. Then Bolt surfaced.

The fight had taken less than two minutes.

He took a further two minutes to regain his composure and then dived to the ocean bottom again, searching for the knife. He found it a few yards from the limp body, which had already risen a few feet. Bolt swam to the sand again.

He slumped near the water's edge, fatigued and in shock. For the first time he had killed another human being, in an act in which he had saved countless others. This time, instead of swimming the man to safety, and working hard to empty his lungs of water, he had fought to empty his lungs of air so that he was sure to take in water and die.

Bolt looked up as several aircraft flew overhead. He felt a pang of fear. Had he been spotted for his act of self-defence? The planes were too high. He could not tell if they were friend or foe. He found himself in the shallows trying to wash off the foul-smelling, cloying black oil while attempting to gather his wits. He shuddered at the thought of the Japanese learning he had killed one of their own.

Bolt looked around the beach. He needed food. The area was fringed with palms. Beyond them he could see yellow fronds. He walked to them and found they were coconut trees. Further on, about 30 yards, there was shimmering green sword-grass, then banana trees with light green fruit hanging low.

He found one coconut on the ground, and was happy for the 9-inch, serrated knife he had just retained. He had thought of it first as a weapon for his own defence. Now he used it to hack open the coconut. He drank the nutritious fluid, and sliced off its white, succulent flesh. Bolt shook another coconut from the tree and sat in the much-needed shade to feed again. Later he plucked a bunch of bananas but considered them too green to eat, except for one, which was hard but edible.

I've had worse breakfasts, he thought to himself.

He was distracted by the sight of a body floating near the water's edge. It was that of his victim. Bolt shuddered at the thought, and wanted to move away. Just as he was contemplating going inland in the hope of finding Dutch soldiers, or even Australians, he saw movement in the water about 50 yards out. Bolt hesitated. If it were another enemy, he was not going in. He strode to the water's edge.

'Mate!' came a cry, 'Help! Mate!'

There was no doubt about the person's nationality. Bolt hurried into the surf and swam to the man.

'Don't struggle,' Bolt said, 'let me take you in.'

Bolt followed the time-honoured lifeguard's drill of getting behind the person so they wouldn't drag the rescuer under. Bolt knew that in nine cases out of ten, the drowning person would struggle with the rescuer. There was no reason in the battle to survive, just instinct. And instinct was to grab hold of anything. Bolt kept talking coolly, never angrily.

Swimming on his back, with the man afloat and his head up, Bolt eased him slowly into shallow water. He put the man's arm over his shoulder and helped him to the sand, where the man slumped. He began coughing up water. Bolt got behind him.

'Relax your body,' he ordered and applied moderate pressure to the man's chest so that he vomited the sea water. Bolt repeated the act, gentler and gentler until there was nothing left in the man's strained lungs. The man was wearing trousers, with one pant-leg shredded. It exposed a bruised and swollen knee.

Neither man said a further word for half an hour. After that time, the man sat up. He shook Bolt's hand, firmly enough under the circumstances.

'Thanks,' he almost mumbled, with a depth of laconic Australian sincerity and brevity, which said so much.

They introduced themselves to each other.

'I'm Al Bright, LS.'

Bright, a leading seaman aged 24 and of average height, had a completely shaven head, one of the few in the RAN who preferred his scalp denuded. His jut jaw and close-set eyes had earned him the nickname 'Bulldog', which he did not appreciate.

Bright looked Bolt over.

'I know that T-bone chest,' Bright said, indicating Bolt's chest hair. 'You saved Red Lead!'

'Not really. That damned animal would have made the shoreline on its own.'

Bright's face flickered a smile. His admiration for his saviour was building.

'Did Collins get her off?' Bolt asked.

'Dunno, sir,' Bright said. 'The captain had ordered him to take the cat with him long before . . . long before last night.' The pain of the memory of *Perth*'s demise surfaced. 'I dunno if Collins made it.' He paused and added, 'I only know that you and me have made it. I saw plenty who didn't.'

'Boatloads will make it,' Bolt assured him. 'Besides, I reckon the Japs will pick up plenty.'

'Dunno about that. A couple of their bloody destroyers nearly hit many of us last night.' He thought again.

'Although I did see one ship stop and send out searchlights, looking for bloody Nip sailors.'

*

Bolt helped Bright, also blackened with oil, to shade under palm trees. He knocked down two low-hanging coconuts and opened them for the new survivor. Bright was wolfing down the food when he noticed a body lapping on the shoreline. He got to his feet with difficulty.

'Leave it,' Bolt said. 'It's a dead Jap. We can bury him later.'

Not far from the Japanese sailor, a 6-feet-long skiff, with curved sides, had washed up. The two men examined it and decided it must have come from an enemy boat. There were scratch marks on the inside. Bolt took a closer look at something on the skiff's floor. He prodded it with a small stick.

'What is it, sir?'

'That's a small animal turd.'

'Are you sure?'

'Pretty well. I've worked in vet surgeries and animal refuges and seen plenty.'

'You don't think . . . ?' Bright said.

'Red Lead? You are an optimist!'

'I do look on the bright side, sir.'

14

BRIGHT AND SHADE

Bolt let Bright rest under the palms and walked along the beach. He had gone about 150 yards when he heard Bright calling. From his more elevated position the younger man had spotted a small boat in the distance. He hobbled to Bolt and they both peered out over the water.

'Japs?' Bright asked.

'Can't tell, although the lifeboat's shape says it's one of theirs.'

'Shit!'

'It may have been picked up by our blokes or the Yanks. It's a fair way out. They may not even get all the way in. It's far too heavy to beat the undertow.' He paused to squint out to sea. 'There seems to be a full load. They'll have to attempt to swim in at some point.'

They strolled on. There was a dead animal just under the surface on the water's edge. Bolt bent down and examined it.

'It's a cat!' Bright said. 'Red Lead?'

'It's been burnt badly. The face . . .'

'Red Lead, do you think?' Bright asked again.

'No. Notice the paws. Red Lead has an extra claw, like a thumb, on each paw.'

Bright sighed with relief. They strolled on. The boat was soon out of sight.

They came across the dead Japanese sailor, which had drifted along the waterfront and then onto the sand.

Bright leaned over it. He bent down and removed a belt and attached sheath from the body. He nodded at the knife jammed into Bolt's shorts. 'You?'

'He drowned,' Bolt said. 'That's all we need to know.' He stared at Bright. 'There are probably thousands of Japs on Java. We don't want them thinking anything different, if we get captured. They'll interrogate us . . .'

Bright nodded his understanding.

'You think they'll find us?' he asked.

At that moment a Japanese spy plane rumbled high overhead. Bolt raised a hand to the sky and said nothing. They walked on.

'What are we gunna do, sir?'

'Rest up for the rest of the first of March 1942,' Bolt said, with the first smile Bright had seen.

'I'm glad you said that. I'm buggered.'

'We've got food.'

'We can make plans tomorrow, sir.'

'Sure, but remember: men make plans; God laughs.'

'You mean . . .'

'Nothing, Al, nothing.'

'Perhaps one of our ships, or one of the Yanks . . . ?'

'Maybe. The oceans around here and Java are ruled by the enemy.'

'Then we are done, sir?'

'Look on the bright side, Mr Bright. There is a reason for everything. Everything happens for the good.'

Bright looked quizzical.

'You really believe that, sir?'

'We survived, didn't we? What have we been spared for? Our ship's company was 681. Sailors love the sea. Most could swim well. I know, I've raced plenty of them.' He paused, picked up a long stick and handed it to Bright, who used it to help himself walk.

A few minutes later, Bolt was alert.

'There's someone out there. He's in trouble.'

Bolt was already in the water.

'What if it's a bloody Jap, sir?'

Bolt ignored him and swam 100 yards out. He stopped to tread water. The man was 50 yards away, his face blackened by oil. He was waving one hand. Bolt sprinted to the man. Close up, he could see he was Caucasian, but in no state to speak.

'Take it easy, sailor,' Bolt said, 'stay calm. You'll be okay. Relax your body, let me take your weight.'

Bolt swam the man in to where Bright was standing in the shallows. He helped Bolt lay the semi-conscious man out on his front, his head turned to one side. Bolt applied pressure to the man's back. Water flowed from his mouth. Bolt kept applying rhythmic pressure to his back. Water kept coming. The man coughed. He spluttered. Bright helped Bolt roll him onto his back. The man heaved hard. He coughed up blood.

'Jesus! He's bleeding!' Bright exclaimed.

'He'll be okay. Drowning victims often cough so much that it causes abrasions inside.'

They carried the man to the shade of the palm trees, and laid him out, his head raised by a rough pillow of palm leaves. After an hour watching over the man, who was snoring peacefully, Bolt and Bright moved into the hinterland.

'Wonder what he's dreaming about,' Bright said.

'Near-naked girls dancing on a desert island, probably,' Bolt said.

Bright laughed.

They pushed their way through thick scrub for about 50 yards and stumbled upon a small freshwater stream. Both men moved into it, using palm leaves to wipe away the oil that had hampered them for the best part of fourteen hours. The viscous liquid had given them both eye trouble but careful wiping began to restore their full sight.

They could not clean up satisfactorily, but at least they had scraped away enough not to fry in the heat, which by mid-afternoon would have been more than 100 degrees Fahrenheit.

They walked back to the third survivor, who was still asleep. They were distracted by more activity in the water. They could make out one man fighting the rip about 200 yards out. Further out, two small craft, one raft and one small boat, were having trouble pushing into shore. They both had makeshift oars, which appeared no more than thin lumps of wood. If anything, they were going backwards.

Bolt turned his attention to the single swimmer, who was making very slow progress. He hurried into the water and swam in the man's direction. About 30 yards from him, Bolt called, 'You okay?'

'Boy!' the man said in a strong southern American drawl, 'am I pleased to see you!'

'Want help?'

'Just guide me in, fella, thank you.'

Bolt swam close. The man was a tall, powerfully built African American in his mid-twenties. He had a small pack strapped to his back.

'Hold on to my shoulder,' Bolt said. The man did as requested.

Bolt breaststroked slowly in with the American holding on just enough to float and without hindrance. They reached the shallows. Bright waded in and helped the American to the water's edge, where he fell on the sand saying, 'Thank the Lord! I did a lot of prayin'. Seems it paid off!'

He reached out a hand to Bolt.

'I'm mighty grateful to you, sir! You English?'

'We're both Australian.'

'Well I'll be! Saved by a kangaroo!'

'Were you on *Houston*?'

The man's eyes welled with tears.

'Sure am . . . was . . .'

'I'm sorry. We were on *Perth*.'

'God knows both of us put up a terrific fight . . .' His voice trailed away.

They helped him up to the palm shade where the third man was resting on his elbows. He was bewildered with what he had woken to and had no memory after swimming and dreaming he was drowning. The man, red-haired Don Farrow, 30, was a Queenslander, who'd joined the RAN a decade earlier and had just been promoted from able seaman to leading seaman. He had a light frame and was of average height at about 5 feet 7 inches. He complained of a stomach-ache and a sore throat.

'You brought up a bit of blood, sailor,' Bolt said. 'Your guts will be scraped a bit. But nothing to worry about. I've seen it all as a lifesaver. You'll be okay.'

The words were reassuring. Farrow looked less concerned than earlier. Bolt explained crisply what had happened to him.

The American, named Edgar Burroughs, was a chef. He opened his waterproof backpack and took out a bottle of bourbon, a torch, a revolver, a mouth-organ, some matches and American dollars. He passed around the bourbon. They all took a swig. It loosened strangulated tongues, and calmed fears, for the moment. Burroughs was apologetic about his job, explaining that African Americans were sometimes restricted in their military service.

'But, heck, I love the *Houston*,' he said, still thinking in the present tense. 'I was happy to serve in the kitchen and in a band.'

'Band?' Bright said.

'Yeah, an all-black jazz band.' He paused and added, 'I wanted to be a gunner. I got my wish right at the end there. I manned the 5-inch battery when we ran outa gunners. All dead . . .'

His voice dropped away again. He was emotional.

'They wouldn't let me do that on account of my colour,' Burroughs added as an afterthought without apparent rancour.

'You mean black, like us?' Bright said, indicating the oil still clinging to their bodies despite their attempts to wash it off.

Burroughs laughed. 'Yeah, right. Where are we, anyways?' he asked.

'Paradise,' Bolt said.

'No, seriously.'

'The island of Java. Dutch East Indies,' Bolt said.

'Correction, sir,' Bright said, 'probably the Nippon East Indies by now.'

'Any idea who was in those boats?' Bolt asked, pointing out to sea.

'I think they were like you, Aussies.'

Everyone paused to scan the horizon. The boats were nowhere to be seen.

There was silence. The four men rested, and ate coconut. They voted to venture further in together at first light the next morning. They bathed in the nearby stream but couldn't remove all the oil, which turned out to be a blessing in one way. It at least kept mosquitoes away after dark.

Just as they were resting, they heard rustling in the bushes. Bolt motioned for them to be quiet. He reached for his knife. He stood just as about six indigenous Javanese emerged from the bushes and stepped close to them brandishing parangs, their machete-like axe weapons.

'Not Dutch!' Bolt said, his hands outstretched in a gesture of peace. 'Not Dutch!'

'American?' the leader, a greying, bow-legged man, asked. And before Burroughs could say he was, Bolt said, 'Australian.'

The natives talked among themselves. They begrudgingly seemed to agree this was just acceptable. But with much gesticulating and pointing, they made it clear they wanted the survivors to move on.

The four made their way down to the water's edge and trudged on until the natives could not be seen in the moonlight.

'What's wrong with the Dutch?' Burroughs asked.

'They've been the colonial masters here for quite a long time,' Bolt said. 'The locals hate them. If we had said we were Dutch, I think they would have chopped us all up.'

'Those bastards scared the shit out of me,' Bright said, rubbing the top of his bald head.

'Me too,' Farrow confessed.

'That's good, then,' Bolt said, 'we'll have no trouble with constipation.'

'Thought we were dead,' Burroughs said, shocked. 'I made it through hell in the water only to be nearly cut to pieces here.'

The four survivors walked on about half a mile before venturing close to the palms again, where they made do with sandy beds and frond coverings. They decided on four watches of two hours each, timed by Burroughs's waterproof Rolex wristwatch.

The weather was cooling and promised a cold night. They discussed making a fire and whether or not it would attract the hostile natives again. Burroughs produced a packet of matches from his pack and they decided to take a risk and make a small fire. Sticks were set in a pile. The fire was lit and the men settled down for an uneasy night, although sheer fatigue soon took hold.

15

THE MISFITS

The next morning at dawn, Farrow, who had the last watch, noticed something in front of the fire, which by then had been reduced to just embers. He stood. From a few yards, it seemed to be a small animal. He moved closer and bent down. It was a dead rat.

'Jesus!'

Bolt woke and joined Farrow. He poked the rat with his knife and flipped it over. There were claw marks around its neck. Bolt counted six indentations on both sides. A bite mark was evident at the base of the skull.

'How'd it get here?' Farrow asked. 'Maybe those damned natives left it as a warning.'

'Special delivery?' Bolt said. 'Doubt it. Had to be a cat.'

'A very quiet one, for sure.'

'Why drop it here?'

'Can't be a food offering, I don't think,' Bolt said.

'Why not?'

'I was here on a boat a few years back. They had a rat plague of some sort. The Dutch advertised for cats to be sent to the island. The cats killed them but would not devour them.'

Dawn uncovered the beachfront. A boat had found its way into the shallows and had been pushed onto the sand. There were seven bodies lying on the sand. Bolt aroused the others.

'We'd better see if they are friend or foe,' he said, sheathing his knife and strapping on the belt. 'C'mon. Safety in numbers.'

The others followed him the few hundred yards back the way they had trekked during the night. They approached the men, some of whom were waking from their slumber.

The seven were Australians. Two were dead. They had died in the night on the beach. The boat had been holed by rocks and coral.

*

These men had fared far worse than the swimmers, except for Farrow. They had all experienced the sickening moments when exploding torpedoes had cruelly ended their lives as sailors and sunk their 'home'. Those in the lifeboat had been on the water for about 30 hours and had endured exploding projectiles, until they were numb. In that time about eighteen vessels were sunk, not to mention the countless numbers of rafts, lifeboats and other vessels which had been reduced, in the main, to driftwood. Sleep had been impossible. They had spent far more time on the ocean, though not in it, than the swimmers. But the latter had kept their bodies moving.

The boat people needed rest. The heat of the day would soon sap what energy they had.

After some brief, hesitant introductions and near enough to a wordless 'discussion', Bolt suggested they move to the shade of the palm trees up the beach, where they could sleep more comfortably. Mosquitoes were already making their presence felt, feasting on a new batch of blood-bearers. The swimmers had been roughly protected by the viscous oil on them and then by sand in the night. But the boat people had no such luxury. They gestured to their lonely-looking boat, now in danger of floating back into the shallows and the ocean. There were mosquito nets and layers of canvas stored in it.

Bolt and the other swimmers pulled the boat away from the incoming tide. They brought the nets and canvas back to shore, along with small barrels of water, one of rum, a tin of kerosene, sandwiches, a bottle of Scotch, biscuits, tins of fruit and tins of bully beef. There were also four oars.

Bolt and the swimmers sat in silence while the others slumbered, snoring heavily. They watched, mosquito nets placed over all of them, as a Japanese destroyer sailed in concentric circles, stopping here and there to observe something in the ocean; perhaps a raft, or a battling swimmer. They were distracted a few times by the not-so-distant boom of artillery. Most depressing was the sight of a seemingly endless, slow-moving line of masts and funnels beyond the horizon.

'Bloody Jap troopships,' Farrow observed gloomily.

'Yeah, probably,' Bright agreed. 'Not ours, for sure.'

'How can you be so sure?' Burroughs asked.

'Well, for a start, our entire 8th Division has been captured. That's a quarter of our force. The other three are in bloody North Africa or the damned Middle East fighting Jerry and the Ities, thanks to fucking Churchill.'

The discussion descended into an anti-Churchill diatribe about Gallipoli in World War I. Bolt brought them back to present dangers.

'The ships mean Java will soon be thick with Japs, if it isn't already,' he said. 'We'll have to work out plans to get out of here.'

'They'll disembark at Priok, mostly, I reckon,' Farrow said.

'That's only, what, 20 miles as the crow flies,' Bright added.

The thought of the enemy's close proximity sobered them to a silence only broken by the steady whine of an amphibious plane. Later they were alerted to bombers and fighters zooming above. No one could tell if they were Allies or enemy.

*

Four hours later each one of the boat people began to emerge from their slumber. First to stir was Pete 'Sparky' Tait, a 23-year-old ship's electrician. The thin man of medium height looked around at the swimmers with a bewildered expression, and tried to stand. Bolt helped him to his feet.

'Welcome, sailor,' Bolt said, shaking hands. 'You've had a rough night.'

'Drink?' he said, his voice husky; his throat parched.

'Water?' Farrow asked.

'No, rum,' Tait said. 'It's in the brown-coloured barrel.'

'We've salvaged it from your boat.'

'I'll go with that,' a second man, gunner Ollie Grout, said, running a rough hand over his bearded face. He was no more than twenty, and unlike most of the callow complexions of his fellow sailors at that age, he already had a weather-beaten look, helped along by endless surfing on Australia's east coast beaches.

Farrow fetched the barrel in question. Soon all the boat people were sitting up, looking around with expressions that were variously stunned, perplexed and confused. Some spoke in brief staccato bursts of horrific nightmares; others mentioned peaceful dreams of death at sea. Mostly they remained silent, trying to make sense of their experiences. They began to feel the heat as the sun moved higher. It was 10 a.m. and already 85 degrees Fahrenheit.

When Bolt judged that some were in a coherent state of mind, he broached the subject of burying the dead close to the palm trees. The others mumbled their agreement and the grisly task was undertaken.

The Japanese sailor whom Bolt had encountered was also dragged to the shallow grave they had scooped out of the deep sand.

'You're not putting that cunt in there with our blokes,' a tall, beefy blond-haired able seaman, Bob Nadler, said. The 6-foot-3-inch 33-year-old had an off-centre, flattened nose that had been on the end of too many bar brawls in his native Sydney. His thick eyebrows gave him a menacing look, even if he was amused, usually by something cruel said about others.

'Then would you like to dig another grave for him?' Bolt asked.

'You cheeky fuck!' Nadler said. 'Who do you think you are?'

'He's an officer from our ship,' Bright said, 'as if you didn't know.'

'He's nobody out here, mate,' Warwick Oscar Wallis, 35, said. He was a thuggish-looking 6-footer with thinning hair brushed back. Wallis was another with a reputation as a brawler and was said to have disabled a man in a bar fight in Perth. He had a distinct, incurable dislike for authority of any kind.

'He's the officer out *here* too,' Bright said, and earned dark looks from Wallis and Nadler. He added defiantly: 'What he says, goes. And it should for all of us.'

'All officers are the same,' Gil Haget, a chunky, 30-year-old West Australian with spectacles strapped to his head, remarked with ambiguity, 'wherever they are.' There may have been more disdain than respect in the comment.

He did not make eye contact with Bolt but instead touched a scar that ran from his left ear to his neck. It was inflamed from the oil, which he kept trying to wipe off. His bulbous nose also had a small scar, which he'd received from flying debris on *Perth*.

Burroughs diffused the potential hostility by pointing at the bodies and saying, 'They're all God's children. It doesn't matter if we bury 'em together.'

'Who asked you, Yank?' Nadler said, turning aggressively to the American.

'Let's take a vote on it,' Bolt suggested.

He asked for a show of hands. Four were fine with the Japanese sailor going in with the Australians. Five were not.

'That decides it,' Bolt said, and began to use his knife to create a second grave a few yards from the first one.

Burroughs fell to his knees and helped, followed by Farrow and Bright. The others wandered off inland to look for food, despite having access to the water and food from their holed lifeboat, which they disdained apart from the rum.

'Be careful,' Bolt said, 'the locals have machetes. They were ready to use them last night.'

Nadler gave him the middle-finger salute and moved off.

'Noted, sailor,' Bolt said, 'noted. Just meet us back here in a couple of hours.'

Nadler ignored him.

Burroughs shook his head and smiled.

'Don't worry about him,' Bolt said, 'all ships have their bully-boys. He was ours. So's his mate, Wallis. Thick, and thick as thieves. Always in trouble at every port.'

'You'd think, at this moment . . .' Burroughs began.

'There'd be more of an attempt at unity? Not blokes like that. We're just unfortunate to be marooned with two or three of the worst types on *Perth*. We don't have many pricks, but they're up there.'

'Prick?'

'Yeah, you'd say "asshole".'

'Okay, gotcha,' Burroughs said with a laugh. 'But I never use the word. My mammy taught me not to cuss.'

'You have better manners than me, Edgar. Wallis is more an arsehole than you know. I'm told he has "W" tattooed on each buttock. His initials are WOW. He likes to bend over and show his mates in the locker-room. Get it?'

'Oh, I do, I do,' Burroughs said with a mock shake of his head.

'Nadler isn't so smart. He has a tattoo of his girlfriend on his calf and one of his mother under it. The word 'Mum' is written between the two small tats. It's hard to work out which is his mother, and which is his girlfriend. No one has been brave enough to ridicule him about it. He is very sensitive about his own stupidity.'

The four men finished the burial job and fashioned two rough crosses from tree branches and bush twine.

Burroughs said a prayer over the two graves. The four men then visited the freshwater stream and washed more of the stinking oil off their bodies.

'Let's see where this goes,' Bolt said, leading the way through the scrub and down a slope towards the ocean. They found two wooden outrigger canoes tied to tree stumps. They were about 16 feet long and 4 feet wide. The men examined the boats, with their upturned bow and stern. They contained two parangs, fishing rods, two paddles, a sail that could be raised quickly, and canvas rain covers.

'Well kept,' Farrow observed. 'Must be owned by local villagers.'

'Made by them too,' Bright said. 'Never seen such unique designs.' He examined a small platform extending from the stern, which held a wooden bucket.

Bolt climbed into one of the canoes. 'One wouldn't hold more than four of us,' he said, sitting on one of two cross-benches, and inspecting one of two paddles.

'Won't make it to Australia,' Bright said.

'Wouldn't get us even around the south of Java,' Farrow opined.

'We'd need a couple like that but a bit bigger and sturdier to take all of us,' Bolt said.

They made their way back towards the meeting point under the palms near the graves, sobered by the thought they'd yet to find an escape vessel suitable for an attempt to make it down a chain of islands to Australia.

They were nearly at the graves when Bolt and Farrow were distracted by something in the bushes. It looked like a wild cat.

'Do you see that?' Farrow exclaimed. 'A black cat.'

They moved closer.

'It's not black,' Bolt said, 'that's oil. It's been in the water too.'

'He must be the one who left us the rat offering.'

The cat backed away.

'Red Lead?' Bolt said, with an upward inflection rather than confidence.

The cat stopped, sat and meowed.

'Fuck me!' Bright mumbled. 'Is it?'

He blundered in the cat's direction. It skipped away and was soon out of sight.

'If it's her,' Bolt said, 'she won't go far.'

They arrived back at the graves. A plump, grey-winged bird, about half the size of a chicken, had been placed between the two crosses. It had also been killed, not eaten. The same distinctive six claw imprints were either side of its neck where it met the bird's torso. Burroughs prodded it with a stick.

'Neck's broken,' he said.

'What do think, sir?' Bright asked. 'Red Lead again?'

'It's her specialty; I mean the broken neck. Maybe it is her. But this is a food offering. It could be cooked.'

'How did she . . .'

'Get here? She's a terrific swimmer,' Bolt said with a smile.

'But not that good.'

'No,' Bolt chortled. 'That skiff we saw; she probably made it on that. Wonder if Bob Collins made it too? Maybe he was with her on it.'

The four men broke open some coconuts. Burroughs, acting as the chef, roasted the bird, and volunteered to sample it first.

'Not bad!' Bright said. 'You're a good cook!'

'That's what starving men always say,' Burroughs said with a bow.

16

INVASION AND REVENGE

Nadler, Haget, Wallis, Tait and Grout made their way along a rough path past the sword-grass that had a layer of humming insects hovering above it; past the banana trees and through the scrub for about half a mile in the sun, at its hottest in mid-afternoon. Sweating and puffing, they came across a village of six poor-looking, flimsy thatched huts spaced about 35 yards apart. Four wells were close by. A few scrawny chickens roamed about, pecking and clucking. The place seemed deserted. Nadler led the way into a hut. They began looking for food. They found potatoes, pumpkins, a green vegetable that was unfamiliar, and some Dutch cigarettes. They stuffed them into a hessian bag.

'Better than the bloody bully beef and rock biscuits,' Haget observed.

Nadler picked up a machete and handed it to Tait.

'Kill the chooks,' he ordered and moved outside to supervise Tait grabbing a chicken and placing it on a tree stump.

114

He chopped off its head. Everyone watched, as if mesmerised, as the bird did a headless dance of death around and through the huts. Tait repeated the act. When the two birds collapsed, Tait stuffed them into the bag.

Ollie Grout sampled water from one of the wells. 'Hmm, sweet enough; not brackish; not that harsh either,' he said as if savouring a wine.

Just as the group was leaving, three young native women carrying bags of washing appeared. They were shocked at the gang of foreign invaders. They dropped their washing and fled into the bush. Nadler dashed after one, and was handling her roughly when Grout caught up with him.

'Take it easy, pal,' he said to Nadler, who had torn part of the woman's sarong.

'She's not bad,' Nadler said, brushing Grout away. 'Haven't had a fuck in weeks! Nice tits, for a bloody boong!'

He wrestled the woman to the ground. She kicked him hard in the genitals and ran off, leaving Nadler writhing in pain. He got up to hobble after her but was restrained by Haget.

'Leave it, mate,' he said, 'you can come back later.'

*

A half-hour later Nadler and his gang of four arrived back at the graves. They emptied out the sack near the smouldering fire that Burroughs was building up.

'Got two chooks in a village,' Nadler said. He pointed to Burroughs. 'Hey, cookie. How about some pluckin' and a roast up?'

'What's the magic word, sailor?' Bolt asked.

'Now!' Nadler said. Haget and the others thought that was funny.

Burroughs moved as if to oblige.

'Let him do it himself,' Bolt said to Burroughs.

Nadler took an intimidating few steps towards Bolt, so that he towered over him. Nadler shaped as if to strike, holding a fist back at shoulder height.

'Bob!' Haget cautioned. 'He's a bloody officer. You hit him and you'll be court-martialled.'

'Fuck that!' Nadler bellowed, the veins in his neck straining. He pushed Bolt in the chest. 'Whose gunna court-martial me, the bloody natives?'

'There are no rules in this situation,' Bolt said, standing his ground. 'I won't be pulling rank.'

'That's big of you, short-arse,' Nadler sneered as he thumped Bolt with an open hand, which caused him to nearly topple over backwards. Turning to Burroughs, Nadler said, 'Do your job, nigger!' He took his eyes off Bolt for a split second. Bolt struck Nadler hard in the solar plexus with a left fist, which winded him. Nadler groaned as his face pushed down and forward, leaving him open to a quick right uppercut to the jaw. Nadler's eyes rolled back in his head. He crumpled unconscious to the sand. Wallis stepped towards Bolt, intent on striking him, but the shorter man was too quick. Bolt ducked, hooked his left leg behind Wallis's legs, and hit the big man with his right fist. Wallis fell backwards and hit the sand. Bolt had connected high on the big man's chest, so hard that Wallis was also rendered breathless.

'Anyone else?' Bolt said, facing Haget, who cringed and held up his hands as if in surrender. 'Remember, all of you. Mr Burroughs's name is Edgar, not *nigger*.' He paused, relaxed his arms and pointed to the gaunt-faced, corpulent Haget, saying. 'You pluck, *please*!'

Later, when the chickens were being prepared, a concussed Nadler began to stir to consciousness. Haget comforted him and Wallis, who was still coughing hard, long after being winded. Haget gave Wallis a sip of coconut juice, which caused him to splutter.

Tait handed Nadler the whisky bottle. 'That should help, sailor,' he said.

Nadler took a hefty swig, and grunted, which was not necessarily a thank you. Wallis took it from him and also drank some of it.

Nadler edged away from the others, his jaw beginning to swell, his face sullen. He said nothing. Wallis, sitting on the sand, eyed Bolt darkly. Bolt walked to him and looked down.

'Let's have it out,' he said, 'right here. I swear in front of all these men, you will not be on a charge if you fight me.'

Wallis waved a hand of resignation.

'You'll keep,' he muttered.

'You bet I will, sailor,' Bolt said, 'Any time you like. For now, it's better we all team up as comrades. We don't know what's in front of us. If you don't want that, you and your mates can piss off!'

Bolt waited. Wallis waved a hand that registered he was staying.

Bolt stuck out a hand for Wallis to shake. He did, but without eye contact or enthusiasm.

'I'll accept that limp shake, for the moment,' Bolt said. 'But it'd better mean something. If we fight, or even squabble among ourselves, we'll have no chance against the natives here, and the Japs when they come after us. And they will.'

The group fell silent. Everyone knew that the muscular, rugged petty officer meant business. He had already asserted himself in the group, and without pulling rank.

Burroughs studied Bolt's expression. His blue eyes, that were steadily on any interlocutor, were serious. For the moment, they gave an unyielding determination to his heavy-set features and otherwise generous, friendly mouth.

'You move pretty good,' Burroughs said to Bolt quietly, out of earshot of the others. 'You been a boxer?'

'No. My old man taught me a few tricks early. His main advice was, don't be a pug, but don't be an Aunt Sally either.' Bolt, relaxed by the conversation that overrode the tension thick in the air, explained the terms and then asked Burroughs: 'Have you been an athlete? You're big enough for American football.'

'I played college football for a few years. But my heart was in another sport.'

'Yeah?'

'Boxing.'

'Okay. But you don't have a mark on you,' Bolt said, indicating Burroughs's face.

'Yeah, well, no one ever cut me up. I was too quick.'

'You fought professionally?'

'I was an amateur. I wanted to represent my country in the 1944 Olympics.'

'Your record?'

'Thirty-one and zero.'

'KOs?'

'Thirty-one.'

'Anyone go the distance?'

'Three rounds was the best.'

'Sailor, I reckon Olympic gold would have been yours for the asking.'

'If anything else happens,' Burroughs said with a nod towards the cabal of Nadler, Wallis and Haget, 'I'll back you up.' He chuckled. 'That's if you need me!'

*

The next morning at first light, Bolt went for a jog along the beachfront and found a lagoon of about 80 yards in length and 10 yards wide. It was clear water, protected from the spreading oil slick by a natural rock formation. He tested the water and found there was little coral. He stripped and dived into water about 4 feet deep, enough for him to swim naturally. He swam 12 lengths, about 1000 yards, and then jogged back to the others who were up and in an awkward discussion about plans.

They all agreed they had to move on, but that reaching Australia was out of the question. Burroughs spoke of his expectation that his navy would turn things around and come looking for survivors. The Australians disabused him of his optimism, explaining that the fall of Singapore a couple of weeks earlier meant there'd be a long wait until the tables were turned against the Japanese.

'After blitzing all the big war shipping from here to Singapore,' Bolt said, 'they effectively control the Pacific and Asian waters.'

'Until we recover from Pearl Harbor,' Burroughs added.

'Agreed. But that will take a few months at least. Let's face it, the British and Australian navies can't beat the Japs without you.'

The key issue for this small group was their immediate survival. They agreed to take the two native boats, which were now shown to the five who had arrived by lifeboat. They would attempt to sail to the eastern end of Java.

Burroughs still thought it would be better to sit and wait for American ships but no one else agreed. 'We've only seen Japanese ships and planes since we got here,' Bolt said. Eventually Burroughs became resigned to travelling on.

None of the nine wanted to take their chances on any road inland that they could find. They knew the Japanese had to be on Java in big numbers. The sea was their least worst option.

'After all,' Farrow remarked, 'we're all sailors.'

*

They were alerted in the late afternoon to more enemy planes than normal flying overhead doing reconnaissance work. As night fell, they thought they heard something in the bushes beyond the palms. The sound of an animal, possibly a cat, was heard. Bolt asked if he could borrow Burroughs's torch. He eased into the scrub calling softly for Red Lead. After several minutes he sat on the ground and waited. Then he heard the mellifluous sound of a cat's meow. He stayed still. A minute later he felt the soft caress of a cat's chin and side on his legs. She began licking his webbed toes.

'My god!' Bolt said. 'It is you!'

He stroked the cat. Her fur was still matted and blackened with oil. Her whiskers and coat were singed here and there, but her character was the same. Red Lead purred.

'How the hell did you make it?' Bolt said, standing and

picking her up. 'I guess I'll never know, unless Collins can tell us.'

He carried her back to the others. All except Nadler, Wallis and Haget made a fuss of her.

'That's seven lives left,' Farrow said.

'Seven?' someone said.

'Yeah. One to make it off *Perth*. Another to make it to shore.'

'It was a bad omen, having her on board,' Haget proffered grumpily. 'She tried to escape at Priok.'

'Bullshit!' Bright said. 'How could one cat's presence determine a battle like we went through? That's an old wives' tale.'

'Who are you calling an old wife?' Haget said.

'You,' Bolt said.

'Don't let the vermin near me,' Nadler said. 'I hate cats.'

'And you were the only one, out of the entire ship's company, who tried to intimidate her,' Bolt remarked.

Nadler looked aggrieved, then annoyed.

'She's not coming with us,' Haget said.

'You bloody well bet she is,' Bright said. 'She's Captain Waller's cat.'

Everyone glanced at Bolt.

'She's coming with us,' he confirmed.

They loaded up the two fishing boats with equal amounts of food and water and began to bed down for the night, about 20 yards from the boats.

Much to Bolt's chagrin, Haget and Nadler, who'd consumed too much rum and whisky to soothe his concussed brain, sore jaw and bruised genitals, decided to go back up to the village to 'look for that little tart'.

Resigned to what Bolt and the rest saw as foolhardy at best and dangerous at worst, he demanded that they arrive back at 6 a.m. so they could push off in the fishing boats at dawn. The two renegades, after sleeping off their hangovers, left the party at 3 a.m., swearing they'd be back on time.

Bolt regretted letting them leave. He had a bad feeling about it.

He began preparing for their cast-off and looked around for Red Lead, who had positioned herself on a rock perched above the boats. Bolt had taken a punt that the cat would want to come with him. Yet he was giving her a choice. She had stayed in the same place through the night, her eyes two small, bright light pinpricks, more green than yellow in the dark. Now he called to her. She meowed, sat up, stretched and made her way to him. Red Lead leapt up into the boat. Bolt gave her pieces of pumpkin and meat. She pawed, eyed and sniffed it. She played with the food as if it were a mouse, then devoured it.

Burroughs took his Colt .45 revolver out of his pack and volunteered to put Red Lead in the backpack. But she would not go in. She moved under the seat where Bolt was sitting.

Bolt noticed the gun. 'Standard issue?' he asked.

'No,' Burroughs said with a blush, 'I smuggled it on board.'

'Please load it, Edgar.'

'Okay, but why?' Burroughs asked as he rummaged in his pack.

'Those two are late getting back . . .'

'Trouble?'

'Nadler thrives on it. He was nearly thrown off the ship for beating up another sailor in Sydney.'

Burroughs loaded the gun and snapped the chamber shut.

17

NATIVE DISTURBANCE

Nadler and Haget got lost on the way to the village and had to return to the beach to reset their bearings. They took two hours to locate the village, only arriving at dawn. They found the girl, no older than sixteen, cooking breakfast in the village square, aided by two older women. Nadler, putting on a charming front, sidled up to her. She screamed. He took a pound note from his pocket and offered it to her. The girl refused and ran to a hut. Her screams roused three men, who had been asleep. They tumbled out of a hut, one with a parang. Haget began trying to calm them down, but with the girl's shrieking and the native men yelling, he had no hope. Soon another three native men appeared.

Instead of sex, Haget now tried to negotiate a safe departure. He offered a pound. The natives snatched it, and gabbled among themselves. They made threatening moves. The parang was waved at him. He gave them another pound note. Nadler began backing away to the track. Suddenly the man with the parang swung it hard at Haget. It sheared through his neck, decapitating him. Nadler ran away as fast as his wobbly, part-intoxicated legs would carry him.

The natives, stunned by their own act, watched Haget's body twist and fall. The head went through several contortions before, bloated and spurting blood, it came to a rest, with spectacles still attached. The women were all screaming now, and for several minutes they forgot about Nadler, who had scampered down the track near the river to its mouth. He yelled for the others—Bolt and his crew of three, and Wallis in the second boat with Tait and Grout—to move out.

'Where's Gil?' Wallis asked.

'He's dead!' Nadler said, his face pale and his eyes wide with fear, as he hauled himself into the second boat, nearly overturning it.

'What?'

'They cut his head off!'

The two boats, with four men in each paddling and rowing furiously, eased through the shallows towards the sea. Just as they reached the surf, about a dozen natives appeared back on the shore. They were gesticulating wildly.

'I'd say . . . we nicked . . . their . . . sea-craft,' Farrow said between breaths. The two boats were making heavy weather of their attempted escape. The natives waded into the water. One swam, holding his parang high.

'Gun!' Bolt said to Burroughs, who handed him the revolver. Bolt waited until the boat slapped down before being lifted by the surf, and took aim at the native only 25 yards away. He fired. The native was hit in the hand. He gave a yelp and dropped the parang. He stayed where he was until the other natives reached him. Everyone examined the wound. Bolt asked for another bullet, reloaded and fired again. The bullet skimmed over the water like a well-directed stone a few feet from the natives. They retreated to the beach.

The two boats, staying within a few yards of each other, reached the open sea with difficulty.

'Look at that!' Bright yelled. All eyes turned to a shape in the water. A shark of about 10 feet in length was circling the area where the native's blood had spilled.

'Shit!' Grout said. 'We didn't see any the other night.'

'The oil kept them away,' Bolt called. 'It's concentrated sludge now. The sharks will move in for the bodies in the clear water.'

The sobering thought silenced everyone as they watched the shark moving close to the natives. They waded in towards the shark waving their parangs, but backed to the sand as it moved swiftly near them, unconcerned about their weapons.

Bolt handed the revolver to Burroughs, who returned it to his pack.

'You're a good shot, man!'

'A fluke. I aimed at his head. The first bullet did the job. The second kept them from being brave and coming after us.'

'You wanted to kill him?'

'I wanted to stop him. They would have reached us. We'd all be mincemeat.'

Burroughs nodded his agreement.

'You wouldn't have done that, Edgar?'

Burroughs shook his head. 'Ain't never killed a man.' He paused, scrutinised Bolt and asked, 'Have you?'

Bright, who was sitting on the front seat with Farrow, looked around at Bolt, who did not reply.

'I guess I would have used it,' Burroughs said, wrestling with his own conscience, 'if they'd gotten to us.'

'That's what the gun's for, mate,' Farrow remarked.

'I guess,' Burroughs repeated in a whisper.

Bolt thought of the irony of a powerful, gifted boxer who had KO'd every opponent in the ring, and possibly damaged a few brains, but who was hesitant about using another kind of weapon. One was used in sport; the other in war.

Bolt rested an oar and patted Burroughs on the back.

'You'd have done it, all right,' Bolt said sympathetically. 'Now, I'm guessing you are a good Christian?'

'I am. Are you?'

'I am Christian, but I've lapsed.'

'It's a good time to believe again, Dan.'

'I like your positivity. You believe we'll get out of this mess?'

'I've been prayin' for it, believe me!'

The ocean was flat further out. They raised their sails but there was no wind. They drifted vaguely parallel to the coast and about 500 yards from the shore. They were all depressed to pass bodies, and body parts, some floating facedown; others just below the surface. They were also disconcerted to see more fins 50 yards away.

One larger shark swam close. Red Lead was sitting next to Bolt. She seemed mesmerised by the 8-foot creature, which was about half the length of the boat. The shark would have been a monster to her. It circled at a distance and looked as if it was going to charge Bolt's boat. Everyone sat stunned and let go a few shocked expletives. The shark bumped the boat. Red Lead moved close to the boat's port side. Before Bolt noticed her, she sat on her hind legs and swiped a tiny paw at the shark as it bumped along the boat's side. Red Lead overbalanced. She bashed her head on the side of the boat but regained her feet, unperturbed and more concerned with the whereabouts of the menacing shark. It moved away. But not far enough for anyone on either boat to relax.

After another two minutes of circling, it zoomed off until it was out of sight. Even still, all the sailors watched the clear water, looking for another furtive torpedo-like attack.

'Did you see bloody Red Lead?' Farrow said. 'She wanted to take it on!'

'Frightened it off, I reckon,' Grout called from the other boat. They all laughed. Even the now morbid Nadler managed a wince. It eased the heart-in-mouth tension, although not enough to stop their vigil on the ocean, looking for telltale fins scything at them from any direction.

'Time for a wank and a biscuit,' Tait said. 'Rum, anyone?'

Burroughs, keen to understand Australian vernacular, asked Bolt what Tait meant.

'Just a stupid sailor's nothing phrase for someone filling in time,' he said with a laugh, 'one takes off weight, the other puts it on again.'

Burroughs repeated the phrase and committed it to memory.

'Goddamn!' he chortled.

Mugs with several nips of rum were passed from boat to boat. It calmed everyone's nerves, which had been shaken by the threats to their lives in and out of the water. Tait asked about his good mate Haget. Nadler shook his head. He didn't want to discuss it.

'They cut his head off,' he finally uttered, almost to himself, his voice unsteady. 'Worse thing I've ever seen.'

The eight men were distracted by the sound of bombs being dropped on Japanese ships which were still unloading troops on Java. Not long after that, a Japanese destroyer appeared on the horizon.

'Pull up the rain covers,' Bolt ordered. Within minutes both boats were shrouded in black veils. The destroyer mowed through the ocean, stirring up undulating waves that held up the two fishing boats. Through slits in the rain covers the eight survivors could see Japanese sailors lining the deck, peering down silently. Some scrutinised them with binoculars. The destroyer picked up speed and moved further out to sea.

The men eased down the rain covers. It was 8 a.m. and their white skin was beginning to show signs of torment from the sun.

They were far enough out from the beach now to appreciate the coast of Java, with its intermittent rock-faces that had changing colours of purple, green and blue. The green vegetation, palm trees and yellow beaches would have been inviting had the men not had such unfortunate experiences already.

The boats drifted apart some 60 yards. More rum was poured for the boat people led by Nadler, whose negativity caused the misery of the others—Tait, Grout and Wallis— to churn. At least Tait, when not rowing or paddling, had a positive distraction with wires, a battery and other parts he had salvaged from the small lifeboat and in his own backpack as he tried in vain to get a radio set to work. Grout's fair skin was suffering in the heat the most, despite wearing a lifejacket and conical hat he had picked up on the beach. Wallis boiled more from within. He was a naturally angry person. Nadler's demeanour caused them all to snap at each other, if they spoke at all.

By contrast, the attitude of Bolt and Burroughs, who already had a kind of kinship, imbued the swimmers' boat with their relaxed manner. They were also less nervous. Even with sharks about they were confident of once again swimming to shore should they be forced into the water.

Red Lead meowed a few times, as if engrossed in her own daydreams. Bolt gave her fresh water, and the bits of pumpkin she loved. She spent a good hour cleaning herself. Her dark brown swirls of fur were beginning to outshine the hideous black muck that had given her a different, thinner, far less attractive appearance.

The rain covers were partially returned, allowing some shade, which the men and the cat took it in turns to share. Red Lead curled up in Bolt's lap as he rowed. She seemed to be enjoying the ride more than her experience on *Perth*.

*

They drifted on through the day. At just about evening, a rainstorm hit and drove them close to shore. It roughed up the ocean, but it was not blustery and both boats were able to stay afloat.

They only had a vague idea where they were, although they agreed they had travelled about 30 miles during the daylight hours, due to strong currents that bounced them along past the landmark coastal village of Anjer. Tait had a scrappy school map, which he had carried with him in the

Perth radio room. He consulted it like a true mariner despite it being from a 1932 classroom.

The question now was whether or not they should pull into land for the night, or sail on, taking turns to lie flat in the boat and attempt sleep. They took a vote. Six wanted to stay on the boat, the argument being that the moonlight would warn them of any problems. There was also a fear that the angry Javanese natives who had murdered Haget might somehow track them by road on Java, although no one had seen a vehicle in the village area. They had seen a bicycle, but just one.

They had one moment of mirth when Red Lead seemed to copy the humans by letting her rear-end, tail straight as an arrow, hang over the port side for a deposit. Everyone except Nadler clapped her effort.

'I love that cat!' Grout shouted.

18

JAVANESE HOSPITALITY

Red Lead was the only one on the boats that fared well in the night as the two boats floated about 100 yards from the shore. The task was made even more formidable by shards of spiked coral below. Despite the rocking, and two of the men, Tait and Farrow, being seasick, she stayed stretched on the floor, only to meow whenever Bolt spoke to her. She shocked him by leaping over the side for a swim in the clear, oil-free water at first light.

'Sharks smell animals in the water,' Wallis warned.

'Hope they have her for breakfast,' Nadler said, loud enough for everyone on both boats to hear.

'You'd be a more interesting meal,' Bolt said.

Burroughs lowered his voice and said to Bolt, 'But bitter, I'd say.'

Bolt smiled. He kept his eye on Red Lead, who ducked under the surface a couple of times, much to the appreciation of the onlookers. After about ten minutes, Bolt beckoned her to the boat. Like a defiant child, she turned away and swam further out. A few minutes later, in her own time, she swam to the stern and the small platform. Red Lead struggled onto it, shook herself and then leapt onto the stern to applause.

'I need a wash,' Bolt said as the cat settled back in the boat. He stripped and dived in, swimming closer to the shore. He was careful to tread water and not step on the coral. He took a moment to urinate.

After a few minutes, there was consternation back on the boats. A shark fin was spotted closer to the boats than Bolt was. He swam into the shallows and rocks. His heart beat fast from the effort and fear. He climbed onto the rocks and watched the shark weaving near where he had been. Bolt regretted urinating. He guessed that the odour had attracted it.

He waited half an hour. When the shark had swum away, he returned to the water, sprinted to the boat and climbed in.

'You're fit, man,' Burroughs said, helping Bolt aboard. His heart and lungs were pumping hard after the effort.

'Amazing what speed you . . . can get to . . . with the thought of a shark possibly . . . right on your tail!'

'I guess you've explained why there aren't any holiday resorts around here,' Farrow said, bringing some much-needed smiles to the gloomy sailors.

Burroughs doled out mixed rations of potato, pumpkin and the rock biscuits. There was no more bully beef. Water was passed around on the swimmers' boat, but eschewed by Wallis, Tait, Nadler and Grout on the other. They opted for rum, again.

Bolt warned them against dehydration. He was ignored.

Burroughs spent some time cajoling Red Lead into his backpack, using pieces of pumpkin to entice her until she jumped in on request, but she wouldn't do it every time. She always wished to display her independence.

*

They were on their way again by 6.30 a.m., hoping to cover more than 20 miles to Labuhan, marked by a black and white lighthouse, just short of Peper Bay, about halfway down Java's west coast. Before noon, the sun was scorching. Both boats had the covers up for protection and the sails down. They were in the doldrums, that low pressure area near the equator between the trade winds. This, along with the rum, the heat and the humidity caused tempers on Nadler's boat to fray.

Nadler refused to take his turn at the oars, claiming that he was not well enough. This incensed Wallis, the ex-Aussie Rules player known for his thuggish acts on football fields. It led to some push and shove that rocked the boat and forced the beanpole Tait and solid Grout to pull them apart.

By mid-afternoon, there had been more altercations between Nadler and Wallis, enough for Bolt to pull his boat close to theirs and suggest they pull into shore.

'Yeah, let's do it,' Grout said, sick of the verbal stoush between the others. 'Sparky reckons we've come 20 miles today, same as yesterday.' He paused and added, drily: 'Guess good old Aussie is out of the question.'

His words were met with solemn silence. It reminded them all of their families in Australia who probably had no idea of the fate of *Perth* and its sailors.

'There's a village or somethin' marked as "Charita",' Tait added. 'It also has a red and white lighthouse.'

*

They reached a jetty that led up to the steel-towered light-house, protruding high on a rocky escarpment, but decided to wait until the morning to explore the area. They bedded down but after a few hours of sleep were woken by a tribe of screaming orangutans, who did not appreciate this batch of humans sleeping on their beach. The sailors threw rocks at them and the primates swung off through the jungle trees, keeping up a racket.

Bolt suggested they attempt to sleep more, but the others were intent on finishing the rum barrel, and taking swigs of scotch. The orangutans' raucous activity had strained their nerves. The alcohol led to slumber, which was only broken rudely the next morning by angry shouting, this time from four Indonesians in semi-uniforms of overalls and caps. They pointed rifles at the eight sailors, who rose carefully from their sandy beds.

Bolt was quick to explain they were shipwrecked Austra-lians, not Dutch. The Indonesians relaxed with this knowledge. One, the chief lighthouse keeper, Amat, who spoke reason-able English, shook hands with Bolt and smiled. He suggested that they follow him to the village at the foot of the rocks that led up to the lighthouse where they would be fed.

Burroughs quizzed Bolt again about the Javanese hatred for the Dutch.

'They have ruled here for about two hundred years,' Bolt explained, 'and they have been quite brutal at times.'

'Like all colonisers.'

'Correct.'

'How many Japs in the area?' Bolt asked Amat.

'Several hundred.'

The Indonesian asked his wife and three effervescent, dark-haired daughters, aged thirteen, sixteen and seventeen, to prepare food, and a half-hour later, the eight sailors were looking at a feast of eggs, pork, salad, rice, fish and chicken and other food. The woman was chirpy and obliging. Red Lead became the centre of attention for the girls. Their father explained that the only cats they'd ever seen were 'big and wild', not domesticated. Red Lead amused everyone by sparring at the family dog, a timid, slow-moving animal that backed away under the table from this new little monster in his midst. She loved the attention, rubbing against the girls' legs, jumping in and out of their laps, and meowing her appreciation. She was offered food by almost everyone, but, showing she could not be bribed, ignored most of it, except pieces of fish. She even waltzed over to Bolt, sat on her hind legs and dug her claws gently into his thighs as he ate. It got his attention.

'Fish!' the girls said, laughing. 'She loves the fish!'

Bolt held a sizeable piece in his hand and, still on her hind legs, she gobbled it up. Red Lead got more laughs when she meowed at him, either as thanks or a plea for more.

'The girls never see foreigners out here,' Amat said. 'We school them ourselves in three languages—Dutch, English and French. Later we want to send them to university.'

The sailors watched with mixed feelings. It reminded most of family life, especially the happy, carefree children. Such personal thoughts were so distant at that moment, they felt almost nostalgic, even if it was only less than a month since they had been with family and friends.

'I wonder if anyone at home knows what happened to *Perth* and us?' Farrow asked.

The others shrugged.

'Us?' Wallis said cynically. '*We* don't even know what happened to hundreds of the crew. We haven't seen anyone else. For all we know they are all dead.'

This observation sobered the table until Grout commented, 'This is heaven. No more green bloody coconuts and the shits.'

'Sure is beautiful,' Nadler said quietly, as he eyed off the pretty teenage girls.

Bolt leaned across the table and caught Nadler's eye.

'You keep your hands off them,' he said in a quiet, firm tone out of earshot of the family. 'We don't want any more of us having our heads removed.' He indicated the lighthouse keeper's rifle resting on a bench outside the family hut and added, 'Or shot.'

The sailors at the table went silent, waiting for Nadler's reaction. He glared back but said nothing.

'I agree with that,' Wallis mumbled, happy to keep up his anger towards the unpopular Nadler. 'You got Haget killed, remember that, over a fuckin' native woman.'

Nadler was about to get to his feet.

'Eat!' Bolt commanded even though they were well into the meal. 'Mr Burroughs will say a late grace.'

Burroughs obliged and defused the tension.

19

MASSACRE

Amat's wife, Ami, would not hear of the sailors sleeping on the beach. She insisted they stay in a spare room in her village home. They were supplied with pillows, thongs, cushions and mosquito nets in better condition than the ones they had cut up and used over the last few days. Ami gave them creams for their bruises. Bright's injured knee had made him hobble. He was most grateful for a soothing potion on the bright red tissue, which he strapped with a clean bandage.

The sailors were taken up 400 steps carved into rock to the lighthouse and shown its operations. Tait noticed radio equipment and was excited to be offered spare parts, especially a retractable aerial that stretched to 5 feet.

He stayed with a young operator working on his radio while the others returned to the house.

'Any news from other lighthouses?' Bolt asked Amat

'The Japanese shut them down or put their own operators in. We know they move through Java on bikes. They destroy the Dutch, who they hate as much as we do. But we don't love Japanese either. We don't want one set of masters being replaced by another.'

After an hour an excited Tait joined the others.

'My radio is working,' he told them, and demonstrated it by using a code to contact the operator in the tower.

*

The family wanted them to stay as long as they wished. Bolt, however, was keen to move on to the south of Java and the port of Tjilatjap, the original destination for *Perth* and *Houston* before they were sunk. Bolt's hope was that they could catch a vessel to Australia from there. Tjilatjap was 220 miles along Java's 520-mile south coast. He was nervous about the Japanese invasion and worried that the enemy could even already be at Tjilatjap.

'It has a "jap" in its name,' he told the others in a joke that was meant as a warning. Bolt asked Amat about the Japanese, and the Indonesian man admitted in a sad tone that they were already seeking to control other lighthouses along all Java coasts.

'They everywhere,' he said.

Bolt decided to stock their boats with food and water and move on.

The next morning, before first light, he walked briskly up the 400 steps to the lighthouse twice more. He then did a half-hour of exercise on the waterfront, including 100 press-ups. He followed this with a swim out about 400 yards and back. He was picking his times to exercise in the early morning and evening in a determined effort to keep his body in reasonable shape, despite their variable diet. This had had a spectacular improvement in the last three days to the point where he had to refuse third or fourth courses from the generous Amat and Ami.

At 8 a.m. he led the sailors, with Red Lead now happily in Burroughs's pack for the time being, down to the boats— only to find them all smashed and the stored food stolen. A note in red was pinned to a mast.

Bolt handed it to Amat. The lighthouse keeper's forehead stretched as he read it. He stumbled over his words, telling them that the Japanese had been there in the night.

'They offer 2000 Dutch guilders for each Allied man captured!' he said, crestfallen. He explained that anyone caught harbouring Allies would be executed.

'We're going now!' Bolt said.

Amat and Ami gave them more backpacks, food and water. Their only choice to continue their journey now they were without boats was by road. The couple then let them borrow four bicycles, and suggested they buy or barter for others. In the village, they bartered two gold bracelets and two watches for more bikes for the long-distance ride east-south-east. Bolt would not consider surrendering his gold watch, given to him by his fiancée after she won two— his and hers—in a singing competition. Instead he paid a village man in Dutch guilders for a bike that had seen better days.

The lighthouse couple's last act was to hand Bolt a fistful of Dutch guilders. At first, he refused. But Amat and Ami insisted he take the money.

'We have plenty,' Ami said. 'You need it more than we do.'

The sailors set off after tearful goodbyes to the family, who seemed resigned to their own fate. They were certain that the Japanese would come for them.

*

Less than an hour after the sailors had wobbled off on the bikes, three trucks full of Japanese soldiers arrived at the village. They dragged the family out of their hut and into the village square, where their sergeant, Hoto, yelled orders and had the family on their knees. He was a short man with a narrow, sharp jaw. He punched Amat and Ami, then questioned them, screaming and ranting. The couple admitted they had looked after the sailors. Their candour further enraged Hoto. Amat refused to tell Hoto which route the sailors had taken. Hoto kicked Ami, upsetting Amat, who went to tackle the Japanese sergeant. He was hammered by soldiers with rifle butts until he was semi-conscious.

The girls were screaming. Some of the soldiers asked permission to deal with them. A worked-up, angry Hoto waved a careless hand. Three of the guards, led by a most aggressive, large and chinless corporal, grabbed the girls and dragged them into the family hut. They tore off the girls' clothes and raped them, the screaming corporal being first to attack each girl before the others.

Ami ran towards the hut, but was stopped by Hoto. She kicked at him. He took out a holstered revolver and shot her in the chest. She slumped to the ground and was soon dead. Hoto stomped in circles around the body. He fired the gun in the air. He ordered a soldier to shoot the ailing Amat. One bullet to the brain finished him. Hoto then yelled for the soldiers in the hut to bring the near-naked girls into the open.

The younger two had fainted in shock. The third was sobbing with bruises around her mouth. Hoto ordered them killed. A volley of rifle shots finished them. He then directed the home be torched.

When it was ablaze, Hoto sat on a chair, breathing heavily after his manic acts. Minutes later, he led six men up the steps to the lighthouse, which was empty of the other keepers. They had escaped down a long safety ladder out of view from the square, having witnessed the mayhem in the village. Hoto supervised as the well-appointed lookout, which would have been useful to Japanese as well as Allied ships, was looted. Every piece of equipment was smashed.

*

Oblivious of the horrific chaos in the village, the sailors bounced along rough dirt roads. They took a pit stop after two hours in another village marked on a map given to them by Amat. Red Lead was released. She stretched her legs by shooting up a tree and attempting to catch an unsuspecting multicoloured bird, which just managed to fly away from her clutches. She made her way back to earth with a most disappointed expression. She sat close to Bolt and began a long self-clean, beginning with her inner thighs and moving on to her face.

'I love her persistence,' he remarked. 'She's winning the battle against the oil. She'll have removed it all in a day or two.'

They were given tea by villagers. An old Javanese man rode a bike into the village. He came over to the sailors and made enough conversation in English to warn them that the Japanese were ahead of them about 10 miles.

He studied their map and suggested a different route to avoid the enemy. He didn't know if the Japanese had taken Tjilatjap yet, but did not think they had come that far.

'Not yet,' he said.

'How many are in the area?'

'Not many—maybe a hundred,' he said with a careless wince. 'You can go around them.'

This did not quite gel with the information from Amat at the lighthouse, who because of Morse code and radio communications around Java with other keepers, was better informed. Then again, Bolt mused, the old man had fresh information about an actual Japanese contingent in the area.

Bolt retrieved the refreshed Red Lead and popped her in Burroughs's backpack. There was no bickering between Nadler and Wallis now, and they stayed 20 yards from each other as they all rode out, two by two down their new track.

An hour later they reached a further village where about twenty soldiers in green uniforms were lounging about drinking beer near three trucks. At first it was thought they were Dutch. But the sailors realised too late that they had ridden into a trap.

The men in green were Japanese.

PART THREE
CAPTIVITY

20

INTERROGATION

The Japanese pointed their rifles at the sailors and lined them up against a hut wall. They ascertained that Bolt was the senior officer of the group. He was taken inside a hut by Sergeant Hoto. They were about the same height. The Japanese officer postured and made guttural sounds as if bolstering himself in the face of a figure his height but far more physically powerful. Bolt was surprised to be offered a cigarette. He didn't smoke but pretended he did. The sergeant seemed thrilled to have Caucasian prisoners. Bolt learned from his broken English that they were the first, other than Dutch, to be picked up.

They were distracted by shouting. They moved outside to see Burroughs jostling with the big corporal who had inspected his pack. He had found Red Lead, who had swiped at the corporal, leaving him with a long surface scratch on his forearm. The corporal was pointing his gun at Burroughs's chest. Red Lead bolted for the jungle and the corporal swung his rifle around and fired at her. The bullet skimmed the ground and split the bark of a tree. Sergeant Hoto stormed over to the corporal and berated him in Japanese. He yanked the rifle from him. It appeared from the one-way conversation that the sergeant was angry that his interrogation of Bolt had been rudely interrupted. Hoto pushed the corporal into the hut and ordered Bolt back in to continue the questioning while the other Japanese soldiers watched the sailors, who were allowed to sit in the shade of trees.

Bolt was careful not to give any information that was not already known by the enemy. Sergeant Hoto spoke in awed tones about the naval battle, explaining that he had heard that many Japanese had also drowned.

'It was a big victory for your navy,' Bolt admitted. The sergeant beamed.

'Okay, but our army better,' Hoto said. 'We defeat China; we defeat Britain. We take Singapore. Now we take Dutch East Indies and many, many countries.'

'Are you going to invade Australia?' Bolt asked as if inquiring about the chances of him going to a soccer match.

'I think so, yes,' the sergeant said with enthusiasm, nodding firmly.

That led into a series of questions about Australia. Bolt, with guile and skill, spoke of how difficult it would be to take his country.

'It's bigger than China,' he said, unsure of his facts but knowing it was at least close in size. 'Lots of problems with desert, no water, no food.' Bolt knew the Japanese were struggling to take China. Suggesting that they might attack another nation the size of China, with extra logistical problems, would give them pause, he hoped.

'Snakes?' Hoto asked.

'Too many,' Bolt said, with a pained expression.

'Kangaroos?'

'Yes. Too many. We eat them.'

The sergeant laughed. He liked the idea of encountering them. He had begun brusquely but as the querying continued, he relaxed. Bolt guessed the man may have been educated and that he had never met anyone from outside his country before.

Bolt managed to avoid answering directly about the Australian military and lied when he had to.

'How many soldiers you have?' Hoto asked.

'One million,' Bolt said, using the figure he had seen reported about the number of people employed in the military, which included those in munitions factories, mainly women. Bolt knew only too well that his country was denuded of defending soldiers, although he'd heard rumours that the army's three remaining divisions could all be coming home from North Africa and the Middle East wars.

'One million is the number of *Australians*,' Bolt said with a frown. 'The Americans will have two million soon.'

That figure was a wild guess. Only non-combatant US troops were in the country so far, but the bluff seemed to work. Sergeant Hoto was wide-eyed at the numbers. He spat facts and figures at the corporal who scribbled, nodded and bowed.

After an hour, Bolt brought up the subject of Red Lead. The sergeant was amused by his concern. Bolt explained the cat had been *Perth*'s symbol. He had been the captain's pet.

'Our captain went down with the ship,' Bolt said.

The sergeant nodded in admiration.

'He die for country. He good captain.'

'He was.'

'We respect such sacrifice. People should die for country. Should not be prisoner.'

'It's a matter of culture. We want to win just as much as you.'

'But you do not die for Australia!'

'Not yet. We prefer the chance to fight another day.'

Hoto reflected on that response, and then shouted: 'You never have chance to win! Japan wins. Japan wins everywhere!'

'This is only the beginning.'

'We should kill all prisoners!'

'It's against the Geneva Convention.'

'We don't bow to that.'

'We do.'

'I think we should kill all prisoners!' Hoto repeated louder and with a sweeping hand indicating beheading.

'You are in charge. You can do it.'

Hoto looked at the POW, with a mix of disdain and perhaps a hint of admiration.

'You can shoot or behead everyone,' Bolt said with a steadfast look. 'But remember, Sergeant, there are plenty more like me where I come from.'

Hoto tried to calm himself down. He lit himself a cigarette without offering Bolt another. He puffed furiously and appeared deep in thought, or emotion. Bolt brought the subject back to Red Lead.

'The cat is also a very good ratter,' he said. He explained with hand movements what he meant by 'ratter'. Hoto appeared relieved to have been taken from a place that pained him. He smiled, then looked serious again.

'Many, many rats in Java!' he said with a shudder. 'Disease! Much!'

'The cat will fight them.'

'Okay, you keep cat!' He turned to the corporal and ordered him to find the cat. Bolt said he would help. The other sailors and the Japanese soldiers looked on as Bolt wandered into the nearby bush calling for Red Lead. After a ten-minute search, Bolt heard a meow. He looked up. Red Lead was perched high on a tree branch. Bolt coaxed her down and, using a piece of pumpkin, talked her into his big backpack, the flap open to allow plenty of air.

Burroughs sidled to Bolt.

'I've still got my gun,' he whispered. 'When Red Lead came out fighting, they didn't look in my pack.'

Bolt locked eyes with Burroughs but did not react.

2 1

BANDUNG

Sergeant Hoto ordered the sailors into one truck with several guards and the rest into the other two vehicles. They drove for about two hours in which the sailors came to terms with being captured. It was a sobering experience for all, whose hopeful thoughts of escaping to Australia were dashed. They halted at a village where there were about 50 more enemy soldiers, who had captured 80 Dutch soldiers. Some of the guards were asleep; others played cards. Occupation of a foreign land had its long downtime.

The sailors were allowed a half mug of water each, but no food. Bolt gave his water to Red Lead. Seeing this, Hoto offered him another half mug of water.

'What is going to happen now?' Bolt asked, keeping any anxiety out of his voice.

'You rest,' Hoto said with the briefest of smiles.

The sailors laid themselves out under coconut trees. The Japanese slung their rifles over their shoulders. They sat and smoked and hardly even glanced at their prisoners. Everyone knew there was nowhere to run. It seemed that the Javanese had been bribed into turning Allies in for money. No one could be trusted.

'You have folks back home?' Burroughs asked Bolt, who stroked Red Lead as she slept on his lap.

'My parents are both dead. I had an older brother serving in the air force. He died in action in the UK. I have a fiancée. She's a singer and dancer in a Melbourne cabaret.'

'Hey, how about that! My gal is a singer! Jazz is her thing.' His wistful expression became one of sadness. 'I miss her like crazy. I have three sisters back home in Alabama . . .' His voice trailed off. His feelings were numbed into silence before he asked Bolt, 'Think we can ever get out of this mess?'

Bolt thought for several seconds before answering. 'Don't know. But the Japs have come out all guns blazing. They appear to have surprised themselves. If they get too cocky, they will have problems.' He paused, looked around and added, 'The Allies are sure to regroup. Bringing you—the US—into the fracas was the Japs' biggest, dumbest mistake. If they'd left you out of it, I mean not attacked Pearl Harbor, I don't think your current president would have had the stomach for war. He remembers the first war.'

The Dutch soldiers, looking dejected, were packed into four trucks which were half covered by canvas. It was standing room only.

The sailors were marched into an empty vehicle. Four guards joined them. Hoto and the rest of his men piled into two other trucks which followed as the convoy moved off north.

'Where we goin'?' Bright asked.

'I think I heard a guard say Bandung,' the laconic Farrow replied.

There was room for a few men to lie down, while the rest stood as the trucks bumped along a dusty track barely carved out of the jungle.

Wallis demanded to know where they were going. The guards stared back but said nothing. Nadler pushed the issue until one guard put an imaginary revolver to Nadler's head and made a sound like a gunshot. This amused the other three guards. A minute later, another one traced a finger across his own throat while looking at Wallis. This drew further mirth from the guards.

'They're not going to . . . ?' Tait asked, his voice tremulous.

'Never know with these little yellow bastards,' Nadler mumbled.

This brought a reaction from one of the guards, who took steps towards Nadler and spat Japanese at him.

Grout said under his breath, 'You silly bastard! I think that bastard understood you called him a bastard.'

*

The convoy arrived in Bandung in the mid-west of Java at dawn after a night as difficult as any they'd had, short of the night *Perth* went down. They had been given rice rations and water, a far cry from the sumptuous meals at the light-house village. For the moment they forgot about nutrition and took in the former Dutch-controlled capital of Java, set between tea plantations and volcanoes 12,000 feet above sea level. The night had been cold, forcing the sailors to huddle close. Now it was cool.

In silence, they observed the town—it had been turned into one big Japanese concentration camp for the Dutch and other Allied POWs. The trucks rumbled past military barracks, squat colonial government buildings and fields where people, predominantly women and children, were imprisoned behind wire fencing. Many male Dutch soldiers were held elsewhere, or were still fighting in the hills. Many thousands had been killed in battle and their families would never see their men again.

The convoy crawled through Jalan Braga, which the Dutch in recent decades had transformed into a prominent street of cafés, restaurants and boutiques. Bandung had been made into a resort town for the Dutch in Batavia and rich Europeans wanting more exotic experiences in an Asian setting. The invading Japanese forces had turned the relaxing boulevard into a near ghost town. The two showpiece art-deco hotels, Savoy Homann and Preanger, were deserted.

The reality of war had been driven home during the naval battles. Now the depressing aftermath of control by a ruthless victor was evident. Still, the solemn experience did not stop the humour. Observing six women in black burqas for the first time, Grout remarked, 'Gor blimey! Six walking letterboxes!'

'Can't be Aussie, then,' Bright said.

'Why?'

'They'd be red, wouldn't they?'

'This is a Muslim nation, lads, despite Dutch religious intentions,' Bolt noted. 'Better to keep such thoughts to yourselves.'

The trucks holding the Dutch veered away to a big open camp, leaving the sailors' truck to branch off, followed by

Hoto and his three vehicles. His three trucks stopped at the Concordia Society, a clubhouse for the wealthy, which had a big ballroom and a theatre. The sailors were unloaded at the latter and pushed into its modest foyer.

It was exclusively for foreigners. Movie posters depicted mainly European films. There were two of American movies—*Gone with the Wind* and *Stagecoach*.

'Gee!' Grout said. 'We're going to the movies!'

There were a few grunts but no laughs from the others. Bolt let Red Lead loose and she dashed about, trying to make sense of yet another new environment.

Hoto took Bolt aside.

'You here for a week, a month maybe,' he told him, his manner even less engaging than earlier.

'And then, Sergeant?'

'I think a boat to Singapore—Changi. You are the first not-Dutch. You will be sent to the place British are.'

He paused and added, 'There will be two guards here. Do not try to escape. I leave orders of shoot to kill.'

It was said with a chilling look. He clicked heels and left.

Bolt informed the others. It was the first time they had learned of a vague 'plan' for them. They had plenty of room in the cinema but no bedding. At 8 a.m. a food truck arrived and they scooped out plates of rice sitting in a pool of thin gruel, along with their one cup of water for the day. Red Lead was offered some by four of the men who refused to eat much of their woeful ration.

She sniffed and pawed it, and then walked away. She returned and began to sample a small lump of the rice, but gave up in disgust, her tail high and haughty. Red Lead looked at Bolt and meowed, as if she were complaining.

'That's what we all think, Red Lead darlin',' Grout said.

The cat meowed again at her name. She slunk off, still unsure about her new home. She disappeared through a door into the theatre itself.

22

TRAIN TENSIONS

At 7 a.m. the next morning the prisoners were awakened by the thunder of trucks moving into the clubhouse compound. They looked through a window to see hundreds of Dutch soldiers being herded into the adjoining ballroom. Before they could digest what was happening, Hoto burst into the cinema followed by six armed guards.

His manner had eroded to something menacing. He yelled for the sailors—'Speedo! Speedo!'—to gather their things and parade outside. Bolt looked around for Red Lead, whom he had last seen moving into the cinema. He hurried there and called for her. He stepped down to the screen area. Two dead rats signalled that she was there. Then he saw her stretched out on a ledge above the screen.

He implored her to join him. To his surprise, she scuttled down the front of the screen to him. He picked her up, and placed her in his pack. He was the last sailor to move outside. Hoto, his manner at complete odds with the day before, confronted and rebuked him. Bolt eyeballed him, which further increased his ire. He removed a sword from a scabbard around his waist. Hoto ordered four guards to hold Bolt on the ground. Bolt warded them off, handed his pack to Burroughs, and then fell to his knees voluntarily.

Hoto waved the sword above Bolt's neck, making threatening, rasping sounds. Then he kicked Bolt in the shoulder, causing him to roll onto his back. Bolt got to his feet, his expression grim yet stoic.

'You go to Batavia for interrogation,' Hoto said in a hoarse whisper and made a sweeping motion with his sword. 'Then they execute you.'

The sailors were given one pint of water to be shared by all of them. The guards pushed them into a truck driven by the big corporal with the extreme short-back-and-sides haircut and tight little moustache who had shot at Red Lead two days before. The sailors had dubbed him 'Little Hitler'. Each sailor was given a thump by an elbow or rifle butt, causing Wallis to utter one of his favourite threats: 'You'll keep, brother.' He received another belt for his trouble.

Hoto did not join them but hurried off to the clubhouse ballroom for other 'duties' with the new batch of several hundred Dutch soldiers.

The truck was driven to the Bandung train station close to the local China-town, which had begun decades earlier when Chinese workers helped build the railway and some of the city's early infrastructure. The sailors, who had not been fed for a day, could smell the chicken, pork, fish, beef and vegetables. They asked for something from Little Hitler. He ignored their requests and pushed each one towards the platform. They stood waiting for a train with hundreds of Indonesian travellers, and a few Japanese in suits. The long train rattled in, looking perhaps as old as the train line, which had been constructed in 1880.

Nearly all the carriages were full for the five-hour, 100-mile journey to Batavia. People spilled into the aisles. The Japanese guards rudely forced people from their seats so that they and their prisoners could sit. All the sailors except Bolt hoisted their packs onto luggage racks. He sat his pack on his lap and opened the top, allowing Red Lead to pop her head out. She wanted to get out. He pointed a firm finger at her, saying, 'No.' The carriage was hot and stuffy, with just two of five roof fans working.

The train pulled out. A woman sitting in a cubicle opposite the sailors pushed out a firm breast for an appreciative baby. None of the sailors had seen such a public display.

'Oh, to be young again,' Bright mumbled, to smiles from the now more relaxed sailors.

Red Lead wriggled free of the pack. She bounced to the floor, only to be confronted by Little Hitler. He pulled a knife from an inside jacket pocket, and made a move towards her. Bolt stood and moved in front of the cat.

'No,' Bolt said, pushing a stiff arm and open hand at the corporal, and staring hard at him. Burroughs and Grout got to their feet slowly. Little Hitler blinked first and put his knife away. He gripped his rifle and aimed it at Bolt. This action caused Burroughs, Bright, Farrow and Tait to stand beside Bolt. Even the antagonistic Nadler and the surly Wallis made as if to help form the phalanx of support. All the guards held their rifles pointed at their

Captain Hector Waller on the open bridge of the HMAS *Perth*.

Captain Albert H. Rooks inspects the USS *Houston*'s band.

HMAS *Perth* I was the home of Red Lead, her ship's cat.

British sailors escape the sinking battleship HMS *Prince of Wales* on
10 December 1941.

The sinking of the USS *Houston* on 1 March 1942, twenty minutes after the *Perth* was sunk by the Japanese Navy. *Painting by Joseph Fleischman, 1950*

The train from Bandung to Batavia in 1942.

Sergeant Peter Chitty, winner of the Changi Brownlow, 1943.

Corporal Wilfred 'Chicken' Smallhorn, 1933 Brownlow Medallist, at Changi Prison.

Dr Frank Cahill (left) at Changi Prison.

Iron trucks filled with prisoners of war en route through Malaya to
Thailand, early 1943.

Prisoners of war on the Thai–Burma Railway, 1943.

Colonel Sir Ernest
Edward 'Weary'
Dunlop.

Trek of the 'swimmers', the very ill and volunteer medicos to Thanbaya.

Prisoners of war at Changi in August 1945.

Red Lead's paw prints painted on the current HMAS *Perth* III.
*Adam Harvey/*ABC News

The silhouette of Red Lead on the bridge of HMAS *Perth* III.
Naval Historical Society of Australia

prisoners. Several Indonesians, fearing a bloody confrontation, moved away from surrounding cubicles. Keeping his eyes on Little Hitler, Bolt bent down, picked up Red Lead and placed her back in the pack.

'Everything okay,' Bolt said, allowing half a smile for the benefit of Little Hitler.

The sailors returned to their seats, and the guards to theirs, but the latter kept pointing their rifles. For the next half-hour, Bolt stroked Red Lead and looked out the window at the villages in the jungle by the tracks. Women were washing clothes in a canal. The scene soon gave way to rice fields and children riding buffaloes. The sight of the yellow-green earth of a big cemetery caused Bolt to glance back to his captors. Little Hitler was snoring in a corner, his rifle sitting lazily in his lap. The guards still held their rifles, but without the intent displayed earlier.

Burroughs leaned across to Bolt and said, 'I may have to use something in my pack.'

Bolt pointed out the window at a man sitting on a platform having his hair cut, as if he were interested in the passing intermittent parade of Javanese humanity.

'Not an option right now,' he said with a false smile.

'I would have used it back at the cinema, if Hoto had . . .'

Bolt didn't respond.

'You showed more courage than any man should,' Burroughs said.

'I thought it was over. I really did. I thought of my fiancée.'

'Did you pray?'

'Oh, yes, very hard; very, very hard.' He chortled. 'I don't think the Lord's Prayer has ever been said faster.'

Burroughs nodded.

'It worked,' he mumbled.

After a pause, Bolt said, 'Can't stop thinking about what Tait learned over his radio from the lighthouse operator. The lighthouse family was massacred.'

'All of them?' a shocked Burroughs asked.

Bolt nodded. 'I wanted to ask Hoto but didn't want to antagonise him. At first, I thought he was fair, but as we got to know him, especially remembering that "beheading" joke with me, I began to think he was capable of anything. He is a most indecent human being.' He paused and patted Red Lead, who was purring. 'That beautiful, innocent family, I want to know if . . .' his voice trailed off.

Twenty miles out of Bandung, the train pulled into a 2-mile-long tunnel, plunging the carriage into darkness. Little Hitler and his men had not accounted for this, and he barked angry orders. When the train shunted out of the tunnel, the guards had their weapons once more aimed at their prisoners. Bolt nodded and smiled at them, as if to say, *Relax, we won't be trying to escape, or mutiny.*

The sailors did half stand to see the valley below. The train appeared almost airborne on the rickety wooden track as its scaffolding swayed in the wind, defying gravity and all the time threatening to collapse, judging from the groans from the bamboo and wood.

An old woman with a food trolley banged her way into the carriage. She had sandwiches and pork buns. The guards bought them and coffee but Little Hitler was adamant that his prisoners could have none.

'Heard the expression, I could die for some food?' Grout said. The others allowed the comment fleeting smiles. They were all famished. An Indonesian couple in the next cubicle noticed their plight. They bought eight pork buns. When the train passed through another tunnel, they handed them out to the sailors, who hid them.

Each sailor in turn asked to go to the toilet and was accompanied by a guard, just in case they attempted to jump off. In the few minutes they were allowed alone each one devoured his pork bun. Bolt took Red Lead to the toilet, used it and urged her to follow. He was amazed to see her go to a corner, scrap around on the non-existent dirt, drop a deposit and urinate. He'd known dogs that did their business when walked, but not a cat, and especially not this one, who had always displayed an almost arrogant single-mindedness. For some innate reason she had complied. He would never know if it was through need or obedience. Bolt cleaned it up, washed his hands, took a good bite of his bun, wrapped it in toilet paper and returned to his seat, Red Lead snugly back in the pack.

The generous and brave Indonesian couple alighted at the next stop, and some of the sailors made sure to nod or mouth a thank you. The guards noticed but were distracted by Bolt offering them some of the sailors' small supply of water, which they declined. The pint bottle was passed around. Bolt cupped his hands while water was dribbled into them. Red Lead lapped it up.

Little Hitler shouted at Grout, who was smiling at something said to him.

'You shame!' another Japanese guard yelled. 'You should be dead. You shame!'

'What's he saying?' Grout asked. 'We are "sham"? What's that?'

'I think he is suggesting we have no shame because we didn't die for our emperor, King George VI,' Bolt explained, a slight tongue in cheek.

'We don't have an emperor, do we?' Bright said, 'I didn't think—'

'Yeah, we do,' Grout interrupted. 'He sits in a palace in London.'

'Well strike me pink!'

'That colour would suit you,' Grout quipped.

Listening to this verbal ping-pong, the guard become angrier.

'You shame!' he shouted and stood.

'You will die for your emperor?' Grout asked Little Hitler.

'Yes!' the corporal spat. 'I die for my country and emperor!'

'Gee, I hope you get a chance to show us,' Grout said, as if he was saying something respectful.

'Hope I'm around to see that,' Bright said with a half bow to the Japanese.

'Yeah,' Grout said under his breath, 'we'll be winning then.'

'I'd break Little Hitler's jaw,' Bright muttered with a fake smile, 'if I could find it. Have you ever seen an uglier person? He's a big fella, but was in the back row when faces were given out.'

'He's like every cartoon in papers and magazines of someone from the yellow hordes coming to invade Australia,' Farrow said.

'They were old cartoon caricatures of Chinese, weren't they?'

'Whatever. Those teeth, mate!' Farrow remarked. 'Reckon they'd match the colour of his backbone. Look like the keys on my grandma's ancient piano!'

The others all suppressed smiles, aware that the red-faced guard could not hear or understand what was being said, but that he could be goaded into using his rifle. Wallis shifted uneasily in his seat. He glared at Grout, then Bright and Farrow.

'What?' Grout said, staring back at Wallis.

Wallis grumbled something unintelligible but surely profane. Then everyone remained silent and turned their eyes to the passing kaleidoscope of green and beautiful mountainous country.

*

They passed languidly through two more tunnels and then several villages in alluvial lowlands. The heat caused all of the sailors to doze. Little Hitler and the guards relaxed their vigil. Bolt was able to sneak Red Lead some of the pork from his bun he'd wrapped in toilet paper. She devoured it with alacrity.

*

The train bumped into the Batavia's (Jakarta's) main station mid-afternoon in extreme heat. The sailors were made to wait with their guards inside the teak-dominated, barrel-vaulted design. They leaned against the brown ceramic walls. Wallis and Nadler lit cigarettes, and refused to offer their fellow sailors one.

'Get your own,' Wallis grunted at Grout. 'You mad fucks will get us all shot!'

23

BATAVIA SOJOURN

The sailors were steered, with more rough handling by Little Hitler, into a truck and driven to colonial army barracks, known as the Bicycle Camp, where a Dutch battalion of bicycle-riding soldiers had been based until a fortnight earlier. Their means of transport sat forlornly in rows, stark reminders of how the war had gone for the beleaguered Dutch. Yet the sailors' modest hut—number 68—in the spacious brick barracks was a surprise for the new inmates. The barracks' red-tiled roofs, verandahs and even a couple of small gardens reminded them a little of home, as did the toilets and running water.

'We've got showers!' Grout marvelled. 'And a bloody toilet where you don't have to stand and balance to crap!'

Tait tried the lights. They worked. There were four sets of double bunks. Negotiations began for positions. Tait was the only one who wanted a top bunk. The others tossed for lower bunks.

'Gotta be a trick in it,' Farrow muttered. 'They give us a great set-up, a meal of our choice and then behead us.'

'Don't be dumb,' Grout said, 'the Nips aren't *that* kind.'

The sailors settled into the hut and were left to their own devices. They noticed Little Hitler and his cruel crew riding off in the truck that had brought them there. A hundred or so Japanese soldiers were in the nearby sports fields.

'We've seen the last of those arseholes, I hope,' Nadler sneered.

'Be careful what you wish for,' Farrow said and pointed to the Japanese playing soccer. 'We don't know what this lot are like.'

Bolt let Red Lead out. Once more she crouched and cringed, looking around wide-eyed at yet another new 'home'. She soon scampered out the door and ran into another cat, a well-fed local tabby. They both stood their ground after the initial mutual shock.

Grout and Bolt were on the verandah, viewing the confrontation.

'Don't worry, fellas,' Grout called, 'I'm sure there are enough rats to go around!'

The cats circled each other, backs arched, with the occasional hiss. After a few stand-off moments they parted. Red Lead was now a half-year old, and almost fully grown. She was bigger than average with powerful shoulders and upper front legs. Front-on she looked like a small bulldog. The local tabby had backed off, even though it would have regarded the hut and its surrounds as its territory. It could not be sure of this intruder.

The sailors were distracted by a dozen Indonesian women, who began to work in a large, open canteen.

'Must be for the Nips,' Tait observed. 'I mean the food.'

'I don't think so,' Bolt said as he nodded to a long convoy of trucks filing into the compound. The first five trucks carried Australians, distinguished by their slouch hats. 'It's the seventh.' He sighed. 'They've been captured.'

The men in the trucks were sullen and did not respond when the sailors waved and saluted. Their trucks veered off to another series of huts in the distance. A set of five more vehicles carried Americans. Burroughs came onto the verandah.

'They're my guys!' he exclaimed. '*Houston* survivors!'

*

The sailors relaxed on their bunks. Farrow and Bolt read two of the English novels left by the Dutch. Tait, on a top bunk, worked on all the bits of radio equipment that he had. He was confident that now he had some relative space, he could produce something that worked. All of them lingered long in the showers, and on the toilets, not having had such luxury since being on their ships. The swimmers were relieved to have removed all remnants of the hated black oil that had matted hair and stuck to skin.

After two hours the group moved down to the canteen, followed by the American sailors. They could buy milk, eggs and some vegetables, along with soap and toothpaste. Some armed Japanese soldiers watched the transactions. Others sat around in the shade smoking, while most lounged in the field watching a scratch soccer match. They were the victors. They cared little for the vanquished in their midst.

The sailors made contact with their fellow Australians in the 7th Division's machine-gun battalion. The gunners were uncommunicative, even surly towards their naval brothers, who soon found out why. Those who talked were bitter and disillusioned. They had been coming home to Australia from the Middle East after fighting there against the Germans and Italians. Under the command of Australian Major General Stan Savige, they had even defeated the Vichy French 7 miles south of Beirut.

'We were diverted here without our bloody guns, which were on another bloody ship bound for Freo,' a lieutenant told Bolt as they sat and ate in the canteen. '"Defend Java", we were told, but what with? We were outnumbered and outgunned. Hundreds of our men, killed for what? Fucking politics. We had to help and please the Poms after Singapore.'

Bolt was sympathetic.

'It was the same for us,' he said. 'We were told to stay around Java to help the Dutch. We were sunk fighting vastly bigger forces. Lost I dunno how many men. Probably three hundred at a guess.'

That impressed the lieutenant, who had no idea of the naval disaster.

'We all wanted to get home and fight for Australia,' he said. 'Look at us now. Prisoners to Imperial fucking Japan and no bloody use to our families, our country . . . Heaven help 'em.'

*

Burroughs had hurried off to make contact with his *Houston* survivors. He returned at dusk, crestfallen.

'Everyone I was close to, gone,' he said huskily. 'All my jazz band—nine of them—didn't even get off the ship. They went down with it.'

He had purchased a bottle of bourbon from the incoming *Houston* sailors and asked Bolt and Farrow to join him in a drink.

'You'll go back to the crew?' Farrow asked.

'I guess so,' the despondent Burroughs said, wiping away a tear. 'God! I prayed for those guys in the band . . . and . . . nothing. All down at the bottom of the ocean . . . gone . . .'

In the evening, Burroughs shook hands with the sailors. Bolt and he exchanged addresses, and began walking together to *Houston*'s barracks.

'Any idea where we're going?' Bolt asked.

'None of the guys know. Rumours are wild. Some say Japan. Others Singapore.'

'Well you are always welcome at our hut,' Bolt said, 'God knows how long we'll be here.'

'Where's Red Lead?' Burroughs said, 'I want to say goodbye.'

The American felt something brush against his calves. It was her.

He held her high. The cat stayed limp and purred.

'I am gonna say hello to you every day we're here, pussycat.' He lowered Red Lead and rubbed her face against his. 'You kept up morale so well. I love you.' Burroughs placed her on the ground. 'Never thought I'd fall in love with a—forgive me Lord—goddamned pussycat!'

Another cat raced by her and she gave chase. Both were out of sight down the avenue within a few seconds.

'Look at that!' Burroughs said. 'I reckon she'd outrun Jesse Owens. I mean it!'

24

PERTH SURVIVORS

Bolt and the six others in Hut 68 were delighted two days later to see about 300 *Perth* survivors trucked into the camp. The new arrivals had cramped conditions in multi-level Hut 8, compared to the smaller but less populated Hut 68. On a vote, none in Hut 68 wanted to move in with their crew, thrilled as they were to know so many of their ship-mates had made it.

'First in, best housed,' Grout observed.

Yet the little group had to join up with the others from *Perth* for work details at the docks cleaning up the debris from air attacks, first by the Japanese, then the Allies. The sailors were also ordered to unload Japanese ships. Few complained. It was not back-breaking work and there was little supervision, with the Japanese leaving that to Australian officers.

Through cryptic, never prolonged exchanges, Bolt's little group learned from the others from *Perth* who had made it and who hadn't. With their numbers being more than 300, hundreds of sailors were still unaccounted for.

The sailors took the opportunity to do some bartering, using their few guilders to buy pumpkin, coconuts and bananas. Cigarettes were harder to come by. Wallis and Nadler, who had gone into his shell even more than before, decided on a method to steal them. Wallis would chat to an Indonesian store owner while Nadler would slip a pack under his shirt. This thieving method was then extended to everything from chewing gum to nuts. Eventually the Japanese commandant was informed. The warning went out that anyone caught taking things illegally would have their hands cut off, which was the method of punishment under Islamic law.

'You blokes had better not do anything with local women,' Grout warned Wallis and Nadler. 'You know what they cut off for that!'

After a week, 495 Americans who had given up once the Dutch surrendered were also brought to the camp. They were flush with funds. A group of sailors from *Perth*, who were not so endowed, set about erecting a line of tents outside their barracks with goods of a wide variety to relieve their American 'cousins' of as many dollars as possible.

Bolt, with help from Tait, who was dragged away from his radio to add mathematical wizardry, set up a roulette school. Bolt was the bank, and with a conflict of interest in play, gambled on the table as well. They had purloined an old, nicely carved wooden French roulette set from a lane of Indonesian stalls near the docks. Boxes of local beer were put on sale next door.

With Farrow as a stooge 'winner', the bank kept losing until about twenty curious Americans, most of whom had never played before, were attracted to chance their arms. They won on a few spins and it looked easy. Then for some odd reason, the bank began to win. After two hours, Bolt, Tait and Farrow had taken about 300 dollars.

*

The weeks drifted by, and the now several thousand prisoners of war made the most of this lull period in which they could live reasonable lives. They occupied their restricted existences with entertainment, including plays and singing. Sport predominated with trilateral competitions with the Dutch, the Australians and the Americans competing in boxing, soccer, volleyball and swimming.

Burroughs, almost true to his word, visited Hut 68 several times a week and found Red Lead, who appeared as happy as any domesticated cat he had seen. She slept ten to twelve hours a day and was not called upon for ratting, mainly because the former Dutch barracks had been kept scrupulously clean. At least ten cats prowled all over the big compound, and Red Lead settled in well in the new surrounds.

Perhaps too well. She joined her feline friends and enemies prowling at night. The wailing was so intense one night that Bolt, Grout and Tait were compelled to search for her.

'I thought she had been spayed,' Tait said, loath to leave his radio set, which he promised would soon bring news.

'Spayed or not, tomcats and their girls just like to have fun,' Grout said.

They found her on their roof. She sat and looked down on them, with a what's-all-the-fuss-about look on her innocent face. Further up the roof, two silhouettes of other cats were slinking about.

'You're grounded,' Bolt said, trying to coax her down with food.

But, true to form, she kept her freedom and individuality. Grumbling, the humans went back to bed. A short time later, the wailing resumed.

'Little minx is at it again,' Bolt said.

'How dare she enjoy herself within earshot,' Farrow said, 'after all we've done for her.'

'Least she's getting a bit,' Grout said, bringing laughs from every bunk.

*

The next morning, Burroughs knocked on Hut 68's door.

'We've got a big swimming meet tonight,' he told Bolt, 'I reckon you could do well.'

'No, I've lost my fitness,' Bolt said.

'You wouldn't win it. We've got an Olympic champ, a Houston artillery man, a Texan, who is unbeatable. He's done under 4 minutes 55 seconds for the 440 yards.'

'What are the race lengths?'

'It's a 50-yard pool, maybe 55 'cause the Dutch are metric. There is a sprint, a 100-metre race, a 200 and a 400.'

'I'll think about it.'

'Can't wait. Got to have nominations by this morning.'

'Okay, I'll go in the 400.'

'Great! What's your best time?'

'Just on 4 minutes 45 seconds.'

'You're kidding! No one has cracked 4.50 yet.'

'That's in America, mate. A few of us have broken it in Australia. Remember most of us live on beaches. We know how to swim.' Bolt was bluffing. He was referring to breaking 4.50 for 400 yards, not metres.

'Yeah, okay, so we'll see you at 7 p.m. Your race is at 7.30 p.m.'

Red Lead was at the door after her hot night on the roof. She slunk in meowing for food.

'Oh, hair of the dog for you, is it?' Bolt said in mock indignation. He wagged his finger at her. She responded with her sensual calf brush.

Bolt took a shower. He laughed when Red Lead wandered in under the water. She stayed there, licking herself.

'Guess you have to clean up after last night, eh?'

Later, over a frugal breakfast of one fried egg, Wallis said, 'I heard you tell Edgar you'd broken 4.45 for the 440. Is that true?'

'No. I meant 400 *yards*.'

'Then why say that?'

'Boasting!' Nadler said.

'Not that.'

'Then why?' Grout also wanted to know.

'Old competition trick, especially in swimming, that my old man taught me. Swimmers are always asking your time for this and that distance. I told him 4.45 so he'll tell this big Texas hero, and he'll sweat over me. The 400 is a middle-distance race and you have plenty of time to play mental games with your opponent.'

'I've heard about this Texan,' Wallis said, winking at the others. 'He's an artillery man, strong as an ox, they say.'

'The bigger they are, the deeper they sink,' Bolt said. 'Besides, in swimming it's the heart and lung capacity that count. If he hasn't got real ticker, I'll beat him.'

'Wallis is bullshitting,' Grout said. 'I've seen the Texan. He's sinewy and tall. Not a powerhouse.'

'Okay, I love racing against a drink of water,' Bolt said, smiling.

'A drink of water,' Tait said, fiddling with his radio set while talking, 'what's that?'

'A tall bloke with weak shoulders and small torso. It means he won't have a big heart or lungs.'

'Spoken like a true short-arse, Dan,' Grout said.

'Yeah, I guess you're right.'

25

ABSENT WITHOUT LEAVE

Bolt and his group walked down the long avenue towards the open-air pool followed by Red Lead, curious to see where her boys were going, and another cat, black with a motley, beaten-up head and chewed ears.

The weather was muggy and still hot, despite the sun having been down for more than an hour. The pool had modest makeshift stands on both sides and was surrounded by hundreds of Allied servicemen. About twenty armed Japanese guards lounged, sat or stood about 10 yards from the pool's shallow end. Many Allied personnel were laying bets on the races.

The 55-yard sprint was won by a *Houston* sailor; the 110-yard by a tall Dutchman, and the 220 by the Texan, Harry Brandorf Jr, who was easily 6 feet 6 inches tall. Big money, at least in terms of this swimming meet, was laid on Harry winning his second event for the night: 440 yards over eight lengths of the pool. There were six lanes for six swimmers: three from the US, two from Holland and Bolt, the lone Australian in the race.

Just before they stood on the blocks, deep-voiced Brandorf, in a red, white and blue one-piece bathing suit looked down at Bolt next to him in black shorts.

'You really done 4.45 for the 400?' Brandorf asked in a Texan drawl.

'Yep, several times,' Bolt replied casually.

'I don't believe it.'

'You'll see tonight.'

The starter, the US naval captain Brett Paul III, holding a starter's pistol, asked the competitors to step onto their blocks.

'Get set!' the starter called as he held the pistol high. There was a disturbance at the shallow end of the pool. Red Lead had jumped in and was paddling around. The spectators laughed. Burroughs made his way down to the pool's edge and beckoned to her. She made her way close to him, and then did a quick turn away, causing Burroughs to almost slip into the water. More laughs. Bolt got off his block, walked half the length of the pool's edge and dived in. He swam with his perfect, ripple-free style that had earned him the Johnny Weissmuller comparison. He held Red Lead and passed her to Burroughs to applause from around the pool.

Bolt stroked slowly back to the deep end, climbed from the pool and resumed his place on the blocks next to Brandorf. The starter fired them away. The six stroked down the pool displaying different styles. One thrashed; one tripped; one made a huge splash with his feet. A fourth sprinted the first lap and touched first. Bolt, breathing on his left, had his bigger opponent in view and was half a body length behind when they touched at the end of the second lap. Brandorf and Bolt were clear of the other four by several yards at the end of the fourth lap. Brandorf stepped up his rating in the fifth, trying to burn off Bolt, who remained almost level with the American. While Bolt's visible stroke did not change, the underwater zigzag movement of his arms quickened. After six laps, they were well clear and it was a two-horse race. The cheering increased as each nation's personnel urged on the competitors.

At the end of the seventh lap, a cowbell was sounded. Brandorf turned just ahead of Bolt and thrashed hard. Bolt stayed close. With 30 yards to go, Bolt's broad shoulders lifted higher and he pounded home, winning by a body-length.

Timekeepers stopped their watches. Bolt clocked 4 minutes 51 seconds; Brandorf, 4.52.5. The competitors were informed. They shook hands to loud applause.

'It was a bit slow,' Bolt said, 'but thanks for a good race.'

'Slow? That was my personal best!' Miffed at the loss, Brandorf added: 'I shouldn't have gone in the 220.'

'Yeah, well, I wish I'd been in that race,' Bolt said as he climbed from the pool. 'That's my favourite, along with the 1500.'

Bolt towelled off. Burroughs handed Red Lead to him as several sailors gave him their congratulations.

'Tried to upstage me, eh?' Bolt said to Red Lead as he carried her back to Hut 68.

The cat meowed and purred.

Back at the pool, Australian punters pocketed their big winnings.

*

Edgar Burroughs knocked on the door to Hut 68 two days later. 'Where's Red Lead?' he asked Bolt.

'Little tart didn't come home last night. She's probably asleep somewhere.'

She was missing all day and the next night. The sailors became worried. Bolt organised a search party and informed the Australian commander, who was unconcerned.

'With respect, Petty Officer, it's just a cat. Strictly speaking, she should not be in the camp.'

'Not true, Commander. She is Captain Waller's cat, and the *Perth*'s mascot.'

The sailors and others scoured the entire barracks. They found six other cats but not Red Lead. A few days went by and there was no sight of her. After a week, Bolt and the sailors feared the worst. After a few more days they believed she was lost for good. They speculated that she had been stolen as a pet or even for her fur. Everyone, and no one in particular, came under suspicion. The other cats in the compound roamed as usual. Her black, rugged male friend sat near the front door one night and wailed on the roof for another couple of nights.

After a fortnight she was forgotten by everyone except Bolt, Burroughs and the sailors, who missed her companionship. They'd been through so much together, especially since the *Perth* went down. For some it was the last tangible link to the ship.

Now, like the ship, she was gone.

26

THE WHEELS BEGIN
TO TURN . . .

Pete 'Sparky' Tait lived up to his name and began to monitor the war from his top bunk in Hut 68 using the radio he had cobbled together. In the middle of the night, and with the transmitter's aerial scraping the hut's roof, he managed to make notes on a BBC foreign service program. In between whistles and crackles that kept the entire hut awake, Tait learned that the Australian Prime Minister, John Curtin, had spoken to parliament about a 'great naval battle' that was taking place off Queensland's coast. The outcome would be of 'crucial importance to the conduct of the war in this theatre'. The BBC broadcast picked up some of Curtin's actual speech. His words moved Tait to tears. He reported that Curtin sounded stoic and strong.

Tait climbed down from his bunk and sat on the floor with the radio still broadcasting. All the sailors, aroused from their slumber, sat with him as the report said Curtin mentioned that Australian and American servicemen were sacrificing their lives at that moment.

Each man in the hut felt a mix of emotions, from impotence to exhilaration. Here at last was a glimpse into the status of the war. Curtin's words presaged a *win*. After months of isolation and idleness there was some hope. The Japanese had chided all the Allied POWs with propaganda at every chance. Now the sailors pondered what the Japanese reaction would be if they had a loss at what was being called the Battle of the Coral Sea.

At the end of the next day, 8 May 1942, Tait was conveying the result of five days of battles between the Americans, supported by the Australians, and the Japanese. Due to the continued propaganda both sides were reporting victories. Tait had scribbled the information on a piece of paper that would be down the toilet moments after it had been talked about in the hut. The Allies had had one carrier destroyed, one almost crippled. One oiler and one destroyer sunk, 66 aircraft lost and 543 men killed or wounded. The sailors could hardly contain their joy as Tait read out the Japanese 'scores'. They lost one carrier and had one crippled. One destroyer and three small naval ships were sunk. Seventy-seven of its aircraft went down. A cheer went up when Tait told the others that 1074 Japanese were either killed or wounded.

The Allies had delivered the Japanese their first major defeat of the war. In so doing they prevented the enemy landing a force in New Guinea and the Solomon Islands. It was a setback for the enemy. The Japanese had been shown to be less than invincible.

'We've gotta let the Yanks know,' Tait said.

'Surely their guys have radios,' Nadler said.

'I've spoken to their sparks. They haven't got the equipment I have.'

Bolt told them not to get cocky or say anything to the Japanese guards.

'I'll drop over to see Burroughs and let him know this evening,' he said.

*

Tait loved being the centre of attention. He doled out data on the hour from the battles and from Australia, and became the chief communicator of information among the Australian sailors and soldiers. Unless the radio was found, the Allied men in the camp would have vital news. Tait let everyone know that the American general Douglas MacArthur had been in Australia for weeks after fleeing the Philippines, where he had been Field Marshal of the Philippine Army, a big fish in a small pond, for several years.

MacArthur's braggadocio manner was scorned in some quarters but he oozed military superiority in the few broadcasts from Melbourne that were picked up by Tait. MacArthur vowed to 'return' to the Philippines a victor, which under the circumstances seemed highly unlikely and was in contrast to Curtin's solemn declarations about battling on. It was what troops wanted to hear and none more than the Allied POWs stuck in an Indonesian camp.

*

Tait picked up comments from Curtin to the effect that a big naval battle—'of unsurpassed significance'—was looming in the Pacific. These words excited the sailors, especially the

Americans. The latter were most confident in the strength of their naval arm. They predicted they would 'clean up the Japs' in the Pacific.

American 'sparks', with Tait's guidance, were beginning to pick up reports from the US, as well as the BBC. On 4 June, the Japanese Navy struck at the American Pacific stronghold at Midway Atoll. The enemy's aim was to attack and take that base and then move on to acquire Hawaii, which they had softened up with a huge attack in the previous December. That would give the Japanese total control of the entire Pacific Ocean. From Australia's point of view, this would cut off the support of their big ally, and allow the Japanese to attack and take Australian territory at will.

Nobody knew anything more than rumours in the Batavia camp until 8 June when 'results' of the massive 72-hour Pacific battle became apparent. The Japanese lost four irreplaceable fleet carriers; the Americans lost one. Japanese air attacks damaged the US Midway Atoll base, but it remained operational. The casualty figures told a further encouraging story for the Allied POWs. The Americans lost 340 men, the carrier USS *Yorktown*, the destroyer USS *Hammam* and 145 aircraft. The Japanese had nine times as many men killed: 3057. Apart from the four aircraft carriers that were sunk, the heavy cruiser *Mikuma* also went down and they lost 228 aircraft.

The American sailors were excited, although many were concerned about losing close friends in such a huge battle. Overriding everything was the sense that the war had taken a sudden change. The Allies could not contain their delight. The Japanese guards, who had for weeks dished out abuse about the destruction of the US, were now chided about Midway.

The reaction was one of fury. Two hundred guards searched the camp for radios, promising the owners would be beheaded. Tait used some duct tape to attach his equipment to the rear of the hut's toilet cistern. He sweated, as did everyone else in Hut 68, when Sergeant Hoto, unseen for months, swept in with twenty guards, including his vicious corporal Little Hitler, who again made a point of seeing that each man was given a jab with a rifle butt. The corporal was more than six feet tall and strongly built, and he enjoyed dishing out bashings. But they found nothing. Despite the bruises, the sailors remained upbeat, which was not lost on the Japanese.

After the Battle of Midway, four US naval commanders were summoned to Bandung to face further interrogation from the Japanese intelligence operatives, who were every bit as ruthless as their German counterparts, the Gestapo.

*

On 12 June, the US navy commanders were escorted by a Japanese guard contingent in a convoy of cars from Batavia to Bandung. Captain Brett Paul noticed an animal on the other side of the road just outside Bandung. It was heading on the side of the main thoroughfare to Batavia. He asked for the convoy to be halted. Paul, with Japanese guards watching, got out of his car and said to an aide, 'I think that's the cat from *Perth*; the one that can swim!'

'Red Lead!' the aide said. He dashed across the road and tried to grab the cat. It was quick to disappear into the bush.

A week later the convoy was returning to Batavia and was a few miles from its destination at the military barracks when the aide spotted the cat again. She was ill. Her coat was dirty. She had two scars on her side. She made to limp away but the aide jumped from the car and this time managed to grab her. He returned her to the convoy. Red Lead did not protest. She seemed too weak.

'My god!' Commander Paul said. 'She's come about 40 miles in a week!'

They drove on. The aide gave her some water from a bottle.

'She was headed towards our barracks, sir,' the aide noted.

'I had a cat like that once,' Paul said. 'She disappeared for two weeks. They say cats have a homing ability like birds. They use their biological clock, the angle of the sun and the earth's magnetic field. They know where home is and can travel long distances to the location.'

'She's been gone for weeks!' the aide said, stroking Red Lead.

'How the hell did she make it to Bandung in the first place?'

'Sir, I think she was stolen, and she escaped from wherever she was taken.'

27

SETTING SAIL
TO *SOMEWHERE*

Hut 68's members were thrilled and relieved to have *Perth*'s mascot returned to them. Red Lead appeared for the first time to be sorry for herself. Bolt examined her and declared she had endured a broken back leg, on which no vet would operate. It had already knitted. She walked with a gait that suggested some awkwardness and possible pain, yet she had not lost any of her spring and agility. Red Lead was happy to be bathed by Bolt and within a few days her coat began to show its previous sheen. Inside a week she was back to her nocturnal prowling on the hut roof with her mates, or mate, the local black male, who was especially affectionate towards her.

More than hope prevailed at the Bicycle Camp. Rumours began that the Allies would soon take back Java. But they proved premature, and there was no further encouraging news for some months.

In early October, the Japanese began inoculating many of the POWs against typhoid and cholera, which indicated they would soon be shipped out. This precipitated further innuendo about where they were going next after the relatively undemanding Batavia camp. It would not be to their own homes in Australia, the US and Holland. A rumour gained credence that Japan would be their destination. Another suggested Singapore. But as the guards themselves did not know, the POWs had no idea. They would not find out even when en route.

Just before they were given orders to march to Batavia's main railway station, Burroughs had a secret meeting with Bolt inside the Hut 68 toilet. He took off his backpack, and pulled out his small revolver.

'I want you to have this,' he said. 'Our commanders are adamant that no guns or knives are to go with us.'

Bolt was surprised.

'You take this pack,' Burroughs said, 'it has the false bottom. Six bullets are in there. You can also more easily leave Red Lead in it.'

Bolt thought briefly and took the pack and gun.

'How will you get Red Lead to go with you?' Burroughs asked. 'We are told, no pets allowed. One of our guys has a dog; another has a rabbit.'

'I have a plan,' Bolt said, tapping his gold wristwatch.

*

The propaganda was subtle. The POWs were told they were going to a recreation-type camp in a very good climate. After the restricted but not arduous life in the Bicycle Camp, this was appealing. The men packed up and were marched to the Batavia railway station, and then trucked to Priok docks, where they waited in the heat to be ordered onto a Japanese ship, the *Kao Maru*, a rust bucket that had seen better days. Bolt was surprised to see Sergeant Hoto and Little Hitler on the wharf.

Bolt asked a guard if he could approach Hoto, but he looked around, saw Bolt and strutted to him.

'Could we please, Sergeant, take a special ratter on the ship?' Bolt asked, bowing.

'No cat. No pets,' Hoto said, his officious face on that morning.

'We hear there are many rats,' Bolt said, as he shook hands with Hoto, slipping 200 dollars into his palm. Hoto pretended not to notice. He stepped away, went straight to a Japanese captain, bowed low and had a quick conversation with him. The captain at first was not impressed and looked irritated. Then he waved a dismissive hand. Hoto then approached another sergeant. After a few words with him, Hoto pointed out Bolt. The sergeant walked over to Bolt and asked to see Red Lead. Aware of the sadistic side that was a feature of some of their captors, Bolt was wary as he lifted back the flap of the pack. The cat popped its head out.

'Very good ratter!' Bolt said with a smile.

The sergeant patted Red Lead, mumbled something in Japanese and marched off.

A sailor a few people behind Bolt said, 'You're lucky, mate. That Nip likes cats.'

The POWs were ordered into the ship's holds. They were humid. There were no portholes. Men complained and received a rifle butt jab for any comment. They could squat, or lie down, but not stand up straight. Soon the holds were packed and many thought it better to lie cheek by jowl. Jokes were heard but in general there was disgruntlement bordering on rebellion. Several of the men had bowel and stomach issues, but were not allowed to visit the one toilet on deck. After two hours waiting for the ship's readiness, men had to urinate or defecate in one of a few buckets passed around. The stench became unbearable and led to others throwing up.

'The party's over,' one POW called.

'Yeah, but where we goin'?' another called.

'The bets are on Japan, mate,' a third said.

'Too flamin' far!' a fourth man said. 'We'd all fuckin' die before we get there. No bloody air in here.'

'Don't forget we're beginning to win the bloody war,' a fifth man said, raising his voice. 'We could be hit by US bombers.'

Bolt squatted and placed Red Lead on his lap.

'What's a fucking cat doin' in here,' one man said and was quickly answered by Grout. 'This shithole is sure to have rats, sport. Then you'll see what that lovely puss can do. Best ratter I've ever seen on a ship. Been sailin' since I was 16. Nothing like that beauty, I can tell you.'

'I can vouch for that,' a cook from *Perth* piped up. 'She murdered Goeballs, the biggest rat we'd ever seen on a boat.'

'I reckon she got rid of all of 'em in the two months before *Perth* went down,' another sailor remarked.

This brought a few cheers when others realised who was being spoken about. The buzz tittered through the hold: Red Lead was with them.

She seemed content to be there, despite a nose twitch. The stench was even a little strong for her, and would get worse as scores of men began to sweat.

When the boat finally sailed, a cautious cheer went up. POWs were allowed up on deck in pairs for a few minutes each. Some men smoked. Others stayed too long and were abused by those in the holds for being selfish. There was a dog-eat-dog feel to the place, and the Australian 'fair go for all' fell away in the first three hours of travel. One man began to sing *Waltzing Matilda*. A second broke out with his own poetry and was howled down after two verses. Later, Bolt was cajoled into the entire 'Clancy of the Overflow'. The men clapped and cheered his flawless, passionate delivery.

Bolt, Red Lead and Farrow went on deck in the third hour. The cat was allowed to roam. As ever, she was in the cautious crouch position to start with. A Japanese guard kicked at her when she came close. She jumped to avoid the boot and scurried back to Bolt.

Towards the end of a harrowing day in which the men's patience was pushed to the limit and the groans of pain and complaint multiplied, the Japanese set a fire hose squirting sea water into the hold. This left everything soggy, but bodies were cleaned a little.

Red Lead drew attention by lapping up the salt water.

'Cats can digest it,' an Australian POW called Noel said. He was a small-framed, short character. He wore double-lenses glasses, which made him look weird.

'Bullshit, Noel!' a voice responded.

'I bet she doesn't throw up,' Noel said.

Bolt asked Grout, 'Who's Noel?'

'Don't know his real name. He always has an opinion, in depth. On everything. He's from Tassie and "Noel" is truncated from "know all".'

They heard Noel say for no apparent reason, 'Cats have twice the number of cerebral neurons than dogs.'

'Jeez, mate. Who told you that?'

'I read it in the *British Medical Journal* of September 1938.'

'You like cats, Noel?' Grout called to him.

'Not particularly. Cats have the same learning capacity as a three-year-old child.'

'You think that about Red Lead?'

Noel thought for several moments.

'Maybe a four-year-old,' he said. 'She may be a freak in the cat species, but not up there with great apes, bottlenose dolphins and Asian elephants, and the manta ray, which has the largest brain of any fish.'

'A freak?'

'There are some in every species, including people like me in the human species.'

There were a few shakes of the head and rolls of the eyes. One POW sitting behind Noel smirked and made a circular motion with his finger next to his ear.

*

The POWs were allowed in groups up to the forward deck for a meal, consisting of rice and a trace of an unidentifiable vegetable, and seaweed soup. They had half an hour on deck. Some wolfed down the meagre offerings and spent the other twenty minutes doing exercises such as leg squats and push-ups to get their blood circulating.

Red Lead amused onlookers when she slapped at the rice.

'Quite right, Red Lead,' Farrow said. 'It's crap.'

She received a big laugh when she sampled the seaweed soup and spat it out in disgust. That brought a roar of approval.

'Exactly how we all feel, gal,' Farrow said.

'I dunno,' Grout said, 'I've eaten dirt and humble pie. They're worse.'

Each of the original swimmers had a small piece of pumpkin, purloined from the Batavia camp, for Red Lead, which she ate.

Once back in the hold, the agony of the voyage continued as the ship chugged along with the occasional roll, which added to the number of men feeling ill.

Noel became the first to declare, categorically, that they were en route to Japan, Osaka to be precise. He had used pencil, paper, a child's atlas and a protractor to track the ship's path.

'Dunno, mate,' Grout said. 'Red Lead's posture when cleaning her ears with one leg in the air says Singapore to me.' Those nearby who heard the comment, laughed. 'Cats' radar is bloody good, you know.'

They all glanced at Red Lead, who went on grooming herself, which she often did for hours on end.

Noel was not amused. Bets went on who was right. Most money was on Red Lead's activity being the correct indicator.

28

NIGHT TERRORS

The evening brought welcome relief from the heat, but the holds' limited air remained fetid and dominated by unwanted, often terrible odours. The night was cold but that was the least of its terrors. An Allied plane buzzed overhead for five minutes and dropped a bomb. It missed but caused the ship to buck and then swerve. The plane made a second, lower run, but missed again. The water surged from the close call and swamped the deck. It splashed into the holds, causing minor flooding. Only Red Lead appeared unperturbed. While the POWs cursed, she jumped down to the floor and sloshed around.

A different, more worrying disturbance came after dark, in the form of the patter of little feet, followed by gnawing teeth. Rats took advantage of the men being unable to stand up. They could kick but usually they struck a fellow POW rather than a rodent.

Bolt allowed Red Lead loose.

'Get 'em, girl!' he urged. The cat ran across bodies and attacked. The squeals were nerve-jangling as she throttled one and then tore at the head of another. POWs called for her assistance all through the hold for nearly an hour. Then all went quiet. She sat in a pool of water on the floor at the foot of the steps, breathing heavily, mouth open and tongue showing. Once she had recovered, she cleaned her paws.

After about a half-hour, she was distracted by one more rat. It came close to inspect this feline serial killer. A torch was shone on Red Lead. She meowed and did not even bother to stand as she pushed two paws down hard using the weight of her powerful front legs, and dug her claws into the victim's neck. The rat choked and was soon dead. Red Lead pawed it to make sure it wasn't foxing. Like a curious morgue attendant, she ascertained that rigor mortis was setting in. Then she went on cleaning. A few minutes later she bounded up to Bolt and landed gently on his chest. He could feel her heart thumping. She was sucking in oxygen in quick gulps. Bolt gave her some water from his dwindling supply. He patted her and whispered soothing words.

He managed fitful sleep, and was woken by the first two POWs allowed up on deck at first light.

'Bloody hell!' one cried. 'Look out for the carnage on the floor. Red Lead killed about nine or ten.'

'You can bet there are more, hiding,' the second man up said.

'Yeah, but super-cat has scared 'em off for the moment.'

The men returned with a bucket and newspaper for a clean-up.

*

The heat of day two arrived fast and dragged on. There were stories of a man dying in another hold. He was, the tale went, slid off the boat in an unceremonious manner.

The rumour spread that their destination was Singapore.

'Red Lead's right again,' Grout crowed.

Another night of chaos ensued. Red Lead had slept about sixteen hours during the day. Her strength regained, she padded over legs, arms and torsos. One POW screamed as a small rat bit the nail on his big toe. A torch was shone on the bloodied foot. Red Lead attacked. After a short, screaming tussle, with the man chiming in with a chorus, Red Lead prevailed. This time, she went to the trouble of carrying the corpse by the neck to the floor near the ladder. More scampering went on. Little scratchy feet and squeals signalled more rodents. Thumps and slides and loud screams registered one wild cat, loving the challenge, for this was sport and/or duty, and not for nourishment. She had yet to leave any evidence that she had savoured her victims.

Not one man complained. By midnight there was no action, apart from the march of the cockroaches that replaced the rats. The latter had been defeated for a second night in the small hold that held about 40 men, and the POWs reckoned about twice as many rodents. Despite only eight rats being dead the next morning, the POWs agreed that Red Lead's ferocity had seen them retreat into hideaways. Most men gained some much-needed sleep, in between the noises of others succumbing to their upset guts.

On the third day, the men were allowed on deck to see Singapore's famed Keppel Harbour, the centrepiece of the hitherto impregnable fortress. The POWs' hearts sank as they noted about 50 ships, all bearing the red-dotted flag of Japan.

'So many bloody arseholes,' Grout shouted, and was told by several POWs to drop his voice.

*

There was a delay when the ship docked. The deck was crowded. The swimmers sat with a few others in a hold. They could see the rats peeking out of holes in the floor and woodwork looking for discarded food. Red Lead wriggled, ready for combat. Bolt restrained her.

'You've done your bit, my beauty,' he said, and the cat relaxed, purring loudly enough for all to hear. She had stopped the rats rushing out, yet nothing, not Red Lead or a nuclear explosion, could stop the cockroaches, who beat the rats to the scraps.

PART FOUR
CHANGI

29

DEAR JOHN

The Australians from 7th Division and *Perth* were trucked to Selarang Barracks, between Changi prison and the township of Selarang near the north-eastern tip of the island. The Barracks had been occupied by 900 Gordon Highlander Regiment soldiers and their families before the war. It had six three-storey, reinforced-concrete blocks. One building served as a kitchen. A small building at the other end of the square housed a clock tower. It had been put on Tokyo time, as had all the other timepieces in Singapore. The island even had a new name, Syonan, 'Light of the South'.

Bolt and the men from Hut 68, still together—Bright, Farrow, Tait, Nadler, Wallis and Grout—had their first glimpse of their new home, billed as a 'holiday camp' by the Japanese. They had been impressed when they first saw Changi's surrounds. The vegetation was lush. Yet two months of pounding from bombs and artillery had destroyed the appearance of the immediate area around the barracks.

The atmosphere was sombre. Buildings were flattened; farmhouses were charred; fields were pocked with craters.

On the first day, prisoners new and old mingled in the square, looking for mates among the 25,000 POWs of Australia's 8th Army Division. There was much talk about who had drowned after *Perth*'s demise, especially by those sailors who had been taken out of the water by the Japanese Navy and shipped to Changi. This led into discussion about Javanese natives, some who had murdered as many as ten sailors. Gil Haget was not the only one to have a horrible end. The men recounted what they had seen. There were a couple of believable tales about killing the Javanese, and even one of knifing a Japanese man to death. Bolt said nothing about his own drowning of one enemy sailor. Bright, true to their original understanding, remained mute on the subject.

'I'll bet there have been more than a couple of Japs cleaned up by our boys,' Bolt said quietly to Bright. 'Like me, they'd be cautious about any loose talk.'

'I think you're right,' Bright said. 'The walls have ears.'

'And perhaps a few traitors open to bribes.'

*

No one, not even the Japanese, knew what to do with the POWs for the moment. They were left to their own devices and organisation. There were plans for barbed wire, but it had been rolled out around only about half the perimeter, and it was not properly pegged upright.

Their captors knew there was nowhere for them to run or hide, if they did try to leave. It was made clear, as ever, that any such adventurers would be met by firing squad or beheading. This was a deterrent for most inmates, although there was already talk of how to get off Singapore. Bravado reigned. Nevertheless, there were bound to be attempts to escape, and bound to be even more executions.

Once again Bolt and his group were able to find suitable quarters—two rooms on a second-floor level with two sets of bunks each. Bright, Wallis, Nadler and Tait took one; Bolt, Grout and Farrow the other. This accommodation had recently been vacated, but no one could tell them why. Perhaps the previous inmates had been sent on clean-up work details in Singapore town. Or maybe they'd been shipped to Burma or Japan for as yet unspecified labour. The timing was good for Bolt and his group, who were pleased. They had a toilet down the hallway. Ceiling fans worked against the incessant sun and hot afternoon breezes.

Red Lead, as ever, had to adjust to a new abode. Bolt took her into the square where a boxer dog, formerly owned by one of the Scottish highlanders, confronted her. He was fat and friendly, but Red Lead was not happy with the encounter. He went to sniff her and she swiped him on the snout. The dog jumped back and appeared hurt by her aggression.

The dog's keeper, a *Perth* survivor, was amazed to learn the cat was Red Lead.

'Christ, she's grown!' he said. 'I first saw her in late 1941. By the time *Perth* went down she was bigger. But now! I've seen cats as big. But not as strong looking in the front legs and torso.'

Bolt soon learned that the Changi inmates were allowed to keep pets. There were several dogs, a few cats, one owl, two guinea pigs, a couple of rabbits and even five snakes controlled by one digger from 8th Division who loved reptiles. Many POWs were allowed birds, some of them

Singapore natives with startling plumage. Red Lead watched them from a second-floor ledge. Her head followed them as if watching a staggered tennis match. She was fascinated, perhaps by the red and green wings, or their juicy size. They would be more of a challenge to catch than the rats.

One day, Bolt watched her slope down the steps to a vegetable garden where she noticed a mouse. She trotted a few feet, and went down on her haunches as if to spring. Then, just as quickly, she lost interest. It seemed that while the rats were fair game, the little mouse was not. She didn't even bother tormenting it with a playful paw.

Red Lead had more trouble adjusting than before. On the second day she explored close to the block and met a lazy brown Siamese cat with blobs of white fur on its head. Red Lead was intent on territorial activity, letting the other know she was already in charge of the second floor. The Siamese, also a female, was most disinterested in such primitive behaviour. She dawdled past the nervous Red Lead as if the new arrival was not there. Red Lead arched her back and hissed. The Siamese didn't even glance back. Red Lead was left sitting and contemplating such indifferent behaviour. It could even have been a snub.

Noel, Grout and Bolt witnessed the cats 'meeting'. Noel, in his usual way, offered unsolicited information.

'They were talking,' he said to Bolt. 'Did you know that cats have a hundred sounds with which to communicate?'

'Had no idea.'

'Your cat said the most, but she wasn't ignored. There was a little squeak from the Siamese.'

'Could you work out the conversation?'

'Not really.'

'No idea?'

'No, sorry.'

'They can't talk to each other,' Grout said, with a head shake.

'They communicate,' Noel said adamantly.

'Impossible. That brown cat is a Siamese, right? Red Lead came from Burma, right? They're two distinct cultures, aren't they? They don't know each other's language.'

Noel thought Grout was serious.

Bolt smiled and said, 'You're wrong, Grouty. Red Lead comes from Mae Sot, a town just inside the Thai side of the border with Burma. They are both from Thailand.'

After the cats' low-key meeting Bolt discovered the owner of the Siamese was an English soldier in another block. His name was Private Harold Pint. He was about 38, and was as languid and listless as his pet. Harold had been in Changi for eight months and was resigned to his fate of ordinariness.

'Better in some ways than back home in Birmingham,' he said to Bolt. 'At least the weather is better.' He had no opinion on the war, except to say, 'Da bloody bulldog [Churchill] will win it for us. Only upper-class I ever admired.'

*

Bolt was impressed with the activities in Changi and the fact that the captors kept well away and let Allied officers maintain discipline. There were schools for everything from languages and highland dancing to cooking and judo. Bolt considered running a vet clinic, and giving some instruction, but decided against it. He'd have to answer too many questions about why he had dropped out of his university course to go sailing. He also feared his lack of formal qualifications would be questioned.

Mail from Australia was delivered in December 1942, and Bolt joined the scramble to see if there were letters for him. There were 43, from family and friends. Only two were from his fiancée, Pamela Steer. He'd met her first when they were six years of age and he'd asked her to marry him then. She'd said 'yes', but then they did not see each other again for nearly three decades until she was making a name for herself as a cabaret singer and dancer. She was, in the Australian vernacular, a 'stunner'. She was a brunette, taller than him, and as bright, although she opted for more artistic endeavours such as singing, dancing and painting. People often told him he was 'fighting above his weight' with her, but he never took such comments seriously. He admired her physical beauty yet it was her vibrancy and sharp wit that attracted him most. She was risqué with her humour, which belied her gentle manner and femininity.

He ripped open the most recent letter from her, which was dated August—making it three months old. He could not believe the content. It was, in effect, a 'Dear John' epistle. She had married another man, an Australian surgeon who had not enlisted. The brief one-pager informed Bolt that she had to tell him, if he were dead or alive. 'You'll never appreciate Bob. But after what he did for me . . . well you know the rest.' Bolt couldn't believe the words, which confused him anyway.

Red Lead, with her typical sensitivity, jumped on his lap and worked her paws on his stomach. He was stunned by the information. He had dreamt of marrying Pamela. Now she was with another. He cried softly. The cat began to purr. He lay on his lower bunk bed. Red Lead hopped on his chest and massaged him again. She purred louder and gently licked the tears running down his cheeks. Bolt felt the rough tongue, and cried more.

He couldn't open the other 42 letters. Instead he went for a long walk around the barracks and the grounds, avoiding conversation with other POWs. After an hour he returned to his room, sat on the sofa, and opened the other letter from Pamela, dated 1 May 1942. Her words stunned him for a second time. In early March, a few days after *Perth* was sunk, she was in a motorcycle accident that resulted in a smashed leg which she had to have amputated.

'I am your one-legged, non-dancing fiancée,' she wrote. 'Can you, will you, still want me, a sorrowful amputee? I ask that not knowing if you are dead or alive! There are so many rumours. One said that everyone on board was drowned. The other said you had all been beheaded. We just don't know. Am I writing to a ghost? It's like praying to God. He never answers! Well, not directly. I had a really good surgeon. He's a "Mister", which as you know is a Master Surgeon. A very handsome one too. Which reminds me. What will you do if you survive? Surely you won't stay in the Navy? Will you finish your Vet degree? . . . I really can't stand writing to a void!'

Bolt had to stop himself from crying again. Hurt as he was, he felt a deep sadness for his now *former* fiancée, who had high hopes that her singing and dancing would take her into the movies. He wished he had been there for her. His eyes welled again when he re-read her line asking if he would still want her.

'Of course I would,' he mumbled to himself, wiping away tears. He felt Red Lead land on the sofa next to him.

When he ignored her, she pawed his arm. He stroked her neck and back, and scratched her under the chin, which she loved. He put the letter down and gave more attention to her. Bolt marvelled at her capacity to understand his moods.

He played with his gold watch, which was inscribed: 'To my true love Dan, forever, Pamela'.

He shook his head.

'Not now,' he mumbled.

He tried to write a letter, and found himself pouring out recrimination, which he knew would be pointless and wrong, even if she had told him to his face, instead of by letter months after the events. He started but did not finish the letter knowing that even if he completed a reply it would probably never reach her.

The whole experience depressed him. He wondered about his future, any future. Pamela had ditched him for a master surgeon. Bolt mused that her mother, who was class conscious and snobbish, would be pleased. She had never thought her daughter should marry anything less. Certainly not an animal doctor and, worse still, a sailor.

30

FROM THE GALLOWS

Listlessly, Bolt opened his other letters, unaware that Grout and Farrow were also doing the same on the room's top bunks. Most of the letters mulled over whether or not Bolt had survived. Many mentioned the 'tragedy' of Pam losing a leg. Her parents reported briefly that she had married her surgeon. Bolt's aunt had kept a newspaper photo of the wedding at Scotch College's impressive chapel but had not sent it to him. However, she noted Pamela was on crutches 'waiting for a new prosthetic leg, which the army said was quite sophisticated, given the number demanded because of the war'.

Later over a cup of tea in the barracks, he, Grout and Farrow sat on the sofa and chairs discussing their news from home. Red Lead jumped on Bolt's lap and began her rhythmic knead on his thighs. Bolt said nothing and just reacted to the others' news.

'Essendon won the flag,' Farrow said, delighted. 'It's their seventh.'

Grout grunted dismissively. 'Who won the Brownlow?' he asked.

'They didn't have one. It's suspended because of the war,' said Farrow.

'Yeah, well, it's not a true competition with so many fellows away fighting.'

'I dunno, they got 49,000 at the grand final. It was held at Princes Park.'

'What? Why not the MCG?'

'It's an army barracks for the war's duration,' Bolt commented.

'Dick Reynolds kicked four for us. Best on ground,' Farrow said.

'Dan's best mate dated his sister, didn't he, Dan?'

Bolt nodded.

'My sister had a baby,' Grout said, changing the subject.

'Congrats!' Farrow said. 'You're an uncle!'

'Yeah, I guess I am,' Grout said with an embarrassed laugh. 'What?'

'Only one trouble, Dicky Pugh, my brother-in-law, has been out of the country for a year fighting in North Africa.'

'Oh!'

'I heard a couple of jokes about blokes in the machine-gunners getting "Dear John" letters.'

'Shit!' Farrow said. 'Wish I'd had one. Me and my missus were fighting so much. It'd be a blessing for me.'

'Kids?'

'Nar. We hadn't had sex for a year.'

'I got one of those letters,' Bolt admitted.

'Yeah, I heard about that,' Farrow remarked. 'Pamela Steer. She married her doctor after an accident. It was all over the papers. A clipping was sent to me. I am really sorry, Dan.'

Bolt said nothing.

'Gee,' Grout said, 'I'm sorry too, Dan.'

'Yeah, well . . .'

'It was reported she said she thought you had gone down with *Perth*.'

There was a long silence before Grout said, 'You always said all things happened for the best.'

'Can't quite see that at the moment.'

'You will, mate. You will.'

Bolt stood, picked up Red Lead and walked out of the room.

'Funny, isn't it,' Grout said to Farrow. 'You'd be pleased if your missus married someone else. He's devastated.'

'Yeah, well,' Farrow responded, 'he wasn't married, was he?'

Grout thought for a moment, then grinned. 'I guess that Pamela's dancing career is over,' he said. 'Unless she goes back to ballet and specialises in the pirouette.'

They were joined by Wallis and Nadler, who had passed Bolt in the square. The story of his being jilted had been a talking point. Another six sailors and a few in the machine-gun battalion had not heard from their wives or girlfriends, but Bolt's predicament was the most high-profile due to the publicity in Australia concerning his fiancée. In the manner of Australia's, at times, caustic male culture, which was heavy on gallows humour, the news resulted in some crude and cruel jokes. Grimness and irony were their hallmark.

'Heard the one about the one-armed paper-hanger marrying the one-legged dancer?' Wallis said.

'No, what?' Grout said.

'They had a whirlwind romance.'

'I wouldn't be telling that one in front of Dan,' Farrow said.

'He's a Collingwood supporter, isn't he?' Nadler said. 'He might like one I heard this morning.'

'Go on,' Wallis prompted.

'Heard about the one-legged bloke who wanted to play for Collingwood? When kicking for goal, he always ended up on his arse.'

'Not that funny,' Grout said. 'Why don't *you* try that one on Dan?'

Nadler didn't respond.

'Guess you wouldn't want your jaw smashed again, eh, Bob?' Farrow laughed.

'What's so funny?' Nadler said in his intimidating tone.

'Nothing really. I just thought Dan might want to get wide-eyed and legless tonight.'

They all sniggered.

'I have another one,' Wallis said, enjoying the fun. 'His girl will have a distinct advantage at Christmas parties and charity events,' he said.

'Go on,' Grout urged.

'She'd win all the one-legged races.'

There were several groans.

'Don't think of a career as a stand-up comic,' Grout said, 'on one leg or two.'

'Aw, fuck you!' Wallis snarled.

*

Word spread quickly about the need for the best rifle shots among the POWs to attend a secret meeting run by Chicken

212

Smallhorn and Peter Chitty, two former Victorian Football League stars, who had set up a competition in Changi, which was attracting more spectators from the 75,000 British and Australian inmates than all the other sports combined. But they were in need of more footballs. Whereas the other sports were friendly affairs, the Aussie Rules games were angry and physical. The participants were putting all their pent-up feelings into hard body clashes.

Chitty cajoled him into attending the meeting on the top level of one of the blocks. They had beer for the twenty men who turned up. Most were from the gunners, who reckoned they knew a thing or two more about firing weapons than any other part of the armed forces.

'We need more balls,' the diminutive Chicken Smallhorn said. He had won the 1933 Brownlow Medal as a rover for Fitzroy.

'I could have told you that,' Grout said, 'you're Victorians!'

The others jeered and laughed. It relaxed the atmosphere.

'No seriously, fellas,' the square-jawed, supremely fit Chitty said. 'We need to shoot wild boar in the middle of the island.'

The room fell silent.

'You're kidding!' someone said.

'No, mate,' Chitty said. 'The bladders are made from rubber, which we can easily nick from the plantations around the place. But we need boar or wild pig skin for the ball's casing.'

'We can acquire the rifles from the Chinese traders,' Smallhorn added. 'They'll guide us into the jungle in the middle of the night.'

There was another silence.

'You telling us the Nips will allow that?' Grout asked.

'Hell, no,' Chitty said. 'They'd behead or shoot anyone caught with a gun. It's bad enough going AWOL all night.'

'Would the traders dob us in?' another gunner asked.

'No,' Smallhorn answered. 'They hate the Nips even more than us. Remember they're Chinese. The Japs have been murdering them by the millions in China ever since they first invaded on a grand scale in 1937. Besides, we'll pay them for the use of the guns.'

Grout leaned close to Bolt.

'You want to be in it?' he asked. 'You're the best shot I've seen.'

'You want to make Red Lead an orphan?' Bolt said.

'C'mon, nothing to lose.'

'Except my head.'

Grout knew Bolt was in a careless, reckless mood after the bad news about his fiancée.

'I'm going,' Grout goaded.

'Okay, I'm in too.'

The next day at 4 p.m. Bolt, Grout and two 8th Division ambulance men, Chitty and Len Lemke, were smuggled out of Changi in a food van and met meat traders in Singapore town. They were taken in a truck to a small valley near a hill north of Bukit Timah, in the middle of Singapore. The four POWs were handed rifles.

It was a nervous time for them, knowing that if the Japanese happened to catch them there would no escaping execution. The Chinese traders led them to a stream in the jungle and told them to wait, hidden in the jungle, until near sundown.

At about 5 p.m. a herd of 250-pound boars came snorting and thrusting down to the stream for an early evening drink.

Bolt got two shots off for two kills. Grout got a third. A fourth was wounded. It turned its attention to the hunters, pawed the ground and charged. The Chinese scattered, two shinnying up trees. Chitty stepped forward, propped, aimed and fired from 20 yards. He hit the animal between the eyes and killed it.

He, Bolt and Lemke stalked three more and made it seven kills in all. The rest of the herd lumbered off, growling. The Chinese traders did the butchering, keeping the meat for themselves. They took the skins to Singaporean craftsmen, who would create the leather for the footballs.

The four Australians were transported back to Changi the next day after spending a lazy six hours in the town near the docks where many POWs were working. The guards did a rollcall mid-afternoon. With all present and accounted for, Bolt and Grout returned to their block for a wash and a meal. Red Lead was at the door waiting for Bolt like a faithful dog.

He picked her up and nuzzled her face into his like a lioness with a lion.

'Why did we do that, risk our necks—for what? Bloody football!' he asked Grout over a drink at the canteen.

'I think it was all part of you getting over your loss.'

'Maybe. But I'm over it now, I hope.'

'No, you're not, but think of it this way,' Grout said, with a smirk that everyone now recognised as the precursor to a cynical or comical remark, 'You've always got Red Lead, and she's got two extra legs!'

Bolt shaped to thump him but managed a rueful smile. This was psychological therapy, Australian-style, mid-war.

*

Tait's radio buzzed, crackled and whistled in the middle of most nights and no one complained in the room. His news was becoming encouraging, even inspiring. The Australians were holding the line in New Guinea and Papua and now pushing the Japanese back. The news electrified the Changi POWs, and the Japanese guards were aware of clapping and cheering in some sections of the prison camp. Guards and officers searched the camp looking for radios.

Tait and the others heard them banging on doors in the block in the middle of the night. He quickly jumped from his bunk, took Red Lead from her basket under Bolt's bunk and placed his radio under her cushion. Bolt placed the bewildered cat back on her cushion, stared at her and told her to 'stay'. This was often a sign for Red Lead to do otherwise, but at this moment she obeyed. The armed Japanese guards knocked hard at their door and were let in. They rummaged around, looked under mattresses, in cupboards and in packs.

Tait and Farrow lit cigarettes in the corridor outside the rooms. They smoked without making eye contact with the guards, who left.

'You must put that thing behind the toilet cistern as you did at the bicycle camp,' Bolt told Tait when they were inside.

'Sorry, sir,' Tait said. 'It's a pain in the arse having to stick it and unstick it.'

'You won't have an arse if those buggers find it.'

There was silence as everyone contemplated how close they were to serious trouble.

'Hey, Dan,' Grout said, 'look on the bright side. The Nips are obviously shitting themselves after the news from New Guinea.'

'I agree,' Bolt said. 'But try not to make remarks to the guards. They'll twig that we're well-informed and raid again.'

The next day, Wallis and Nadler were leaning over the fence to a sports field where a Japanese soccer match was being played.

'What's it feel like to be losing?' Wallis called to a Japanese spectator. He looked confused and discussed what was said with others. Three guards stood, picked up rifles, and moved to the two Australians.

'What you say?' one guard said. 'These both Japan teams.'

'Oh,' Nadler said, 'we thought one team was Korean.'

'Sorry,' Wallis said, 'my mistake. I thought Japan was losing.'

Nadler nudged Wallis, and indicated they should leave.

'You're a stupid bugger,' Nadler said. 'They'll work out what you meant, and then they'll raid us again.'

31

TRAIN OF PAIN

In mid-February 1943, about 100 of the *Perth* sailors, including Bolt and his group, and 200 of the 7th Division machine-gunners were ordered into trucks at Changi and taken to Singapore railway station. There was a heavy mist over the harbour, which threatened rain. The POWs looked wistfully, with a trace of distant lust, at Chinese women, wearing yellow conical hats, red tops, discreet long blue skirts and black thongs.

'Are you thinking what I'm thinking?' Farrow said to Grout.

'God! I hope not!'

'Some of them looked sweet.'

'No way!'

'What?'

'I'm a Richmond fan, yellow and black. They're in Melbourne colours.'

The POWs had been promised plentiful food, fabulous Thai countryside and there was even mention of beautiful women, if they helped build a mighty railway for the Emperor, although it was not specified if he would ever see it. They could bring gramophones, blankets, clothing and mosquito nets. There would be no long marches. Transport would be provided for unfit men and luggage. Good canteens, always a selling point, would be at each work area. This workforce was one of the early ones but not the first. The Japanese had learned to make the project look enticing. In a sudden effort to step up the railway construction, which would run 280 miles over much difficult mountainous terrain and deep valleys, ill prisoners were allowed to join the group. The reasoning from the captors was that the task would be in such lovely conditions that the sufferers of malaria, beri-beri, dysentery and a dozen other ailments, including little understood mental illnesses, would be cured.

Very few of the POWs bought the propaganda. They had heard rumours that the Thai experience would be horrific, but for many it was a chance to move on from the confines of Changi. *Perth*'s sailors were being splintered into small work groups, and sent to a variety of places in Burma, Thailand and Japan. Bolt's group, despite some differences among them, stayed together for the Thailand venture.

As they waited at the station, Japanese spokesmen, with their struggling English pronunciation, began to provide a different picture of their journey.

'Thais are thieves,' the POWs were told, 'keep hold of all possessions. Thais like footwear. They will steal your boots.'

They were informed of a strict no pets rule. Bolt, with Red Lead perched neatly inside his pack, had one small bargaining chip left, along with 200 of the American dollars he'd won in roulette games in Changi.

Grout, Tait and Farrow were nervous for him and the cat.

'What are you going to do?' Grout whispered as they waited.

'Pray?' Bolt said, noticing a Japanese sergeant who would be in charge of the train they would soon be taking.

'That's bloody Hoto, isn't it?' Tait said first.

'And fucking Little Hitler with him.' Nadler groaned. 'God bugger me dead! Those bastards!'

Bolt stepped out of the line and called, 'Sergeant Hoto, over here.'

Hoto looked around sharply and marched to Bolt.

'Not feeling too well,' Bolt said. 'Is there a sick bay?'

He pressed the money into Hoto's hand.

Hoto didn't react. He bellowed for Little Hitler to take Bolt on board, and followed them into a carriage. Little Hitler was dismissed. Hoto asked what he wanted.

Bolt loosened his wristwatch.

'This is pure gold,' he said under his breath. 'I want you to have it.'

Hoto examined it.

'Why?' he said with a dead stare.

'You will be able to sell it on the black market for five hundred American dollars. Very expensive. Try it on.'

Hoto did so.

'Looks so good on you, Sergeant.'

Hoto glanced at Bolt's pack, but said nothing and the two men returned to the wharf. The POWs were given a long list of rules for the Thai assignment. They included no animals being allowed. Bolt was nervous about the mercurial

Hoto double-crossing him about Red Lead. The cat, for her part, was not moving in the pack. It was hot. Bolt opened the top a little more and patted her. She was sleeping. Her breathing was not laboured. Red Lead was getting used to the travel. As long as she was with her small tribe of humans, she was content.

At 2 p.m. the men were ordered into closed iron carriages, with two open carriages for the Japanese guards controlled by Hoto. The train jolted off across Singapore island, causing some POWs to lose their footing.

'Bloody Jap driver,' someone complained.

'Give him a break,' Grout said, 'the train has square wheels.'

A couple of POWs glanced at him, unsure if he was serious. Seeing this, Grout added, 'Haven't invented round ones here, yet.'

The men complained to the one Japanese guard about the heat. He opened the sliding door about 2 feet. The POWs took it in turns to look out at the scenery, which was at times depressing. Big oil trucks had been flattened like tin cans, and now sat in black pools far too familiar to the sailors. Hundreds of women were doing the dirty work of cleaning up after the men of war.

They reached the causeway joining the island to Malaya. It had been partially broken up by bombs from the retreating British, Indians and Australians. The train passed the Sultan of Johor's palace, with its square tower, from which the Japanese had planned Singapore's invasion and destruction.

'The guys in the eighth wanted to blow that palace,' a soldier said, 'but the flamin' British wouldn't let 'em. Didn't want to upset the sultan and his bloody harem, hundreds of young, gorgeous women.'

No one knew if this was true or not, but it sounded good to the companion-starved POWs.

'We can always pick 'em up on the way back,' Grout said, giving the thirsty men a laugh, and a fleeting covetous thought, or three.

The men soon stopped viewing the land, which was just miles of monotonous green rubber plantations.

*

The first leg of the journey was broken up by two pit stops, in which the POWs were ordered to 'do their business'.

'Crap on demand, fellas,' a POW said, 'or forever hold thy stink.'

Bolt opened the pack to allow Red Lead her moment.

'Geez, you've let the cat out of the bag now, mate,' someone said. Bolt was too busy to respond. He had one eye on Red Lead, who obliged his urgings, while relieving himself.

Red Lead in diligent, hygienic cat fashion, scrapped over her deposit.

'Hey, Red Lead,' one man called, 'can you do mine too?'

She sniffed around, bent low. Bolt grabbed her and placed her back in the pack, making sure she had enough satisfying sips of water from his bottle.

*

The cramped journey continued for many hours until they reached a further stopping point at midnight. As they filed out of the train to a platform, someone asked where they were.

'Gemas,' the guard said.

'Gemas or Venice?' Grout said, but there were no laughs. The men were fatigued. They were livened a fraction by food, the usual rice fare, but with a dash of something green, which could have been curry soup.

'My gosh,' a POW remarked, 'this has flavour.'

'Yeah, dog vomit,' came an unpopular reply.

After almost an hour's break the irritated, increasingly silent POWs were steered to the carriages again for the onward journey of seven hours to the Malayan capital of Kuala Lumpur.

Their arrival there saw the men stampede for the water tower. They yanked down a hose which poured out the life-giving liquid. It was variously drunk or used to wash by hundreds of dirty travellers. Bolt hung back, not wanting Red Lead to get swamped or drowned in the rush and crush. He took her gently from the bag. She was drowsy. She recovered and, to Bolt's shock, rushed to joined the milling rugby scrum in the communal shower. Guards waded in, punching and belting the POWs, one of whom stood on Red Lead's tail. She gave a high-pitched yelp. Drenched, she dashed to the worried Bolt. But he did not scold her. She needed a reassuring pat on her wet, matted fur.

Once order was restored, the men were given their breakfast, which was the same gruel of rice and green curry-tasting soup. Some men had a bad reaction even before continuing the journey, and the train was held up while they vomited or defecated.

*

The next leg, in bright sunshine, saw the metal door opened even further. More rubber plantations were replaced with hills and valleys of various shades of green, with the odd farm visible. The war had been over here for nearly a year, but evidence of it was strewn everywhere. A long graveyard of cars, interspersed with tanks of some sort, predominated. The men were aroused by the occasional sight of downed Japanese fighter planes, broken like kids' abandoned toys. There were happy gasps and finger-pointing directed at the Japanese guard, who knew what was exciting his charges.

There was nothing he could do and would be overwhelmed if he attacked anyone. He glared or looked away. He became angry and threatened to close the door. The guard seemed apprehensive, as if he could be rushed and thrown out of the moving train.

The heat made most of the POWs listless and they slept fitfully, only to be bundled out for two more pit stops, and then, at 9.30 p.m., they were offered the inevitable rice meal, at Ipoh. There was another scramble for the water tower. Bolt wandered away from it to let Red Lead stretch. He was concerned she would disappear in the dark.

*

The dispiriting travel became a serious grind for the ill, and even the fit men. Finding water became the main concern and Bolt and his group made sure they filled their bottles at each stop. Another night, followed by breakfast, took them deeper into Malaya and closer to their destination, the promised Thailand.

Rice fields, duller and more monochrome than even the rubber plantations, took over. The terrain became more rugged, but the men were too bored, listless and disgruntled to take much of it in. The days were suffocating; the nights cold, and the men were glad of even their thin blankets.

The only relief came from Bolt reciting every stanza of Banjo Paterson's 'The Man from Snowy River', with the same spirit he'd delivered 'Clancy' earlier. That encouraged singing and football songs, along with howls of protest. The guard looked on, perplexed at these very strange, rugged humans from Australia who'd rather endure this hardship than die for their king. Yet the guard smiled for the first time at a stirring rendition of 'Waltzing Matilda', followed by 'Jingle Bells', 'It's a Long Way to Tipperary' and 'Where the Dog Sits on the Tuckerbox'. Not all of them knew the words for each, yet they sang along. It brightened them for an hour, and even the guard received a cheer when urged to join in with words he didn't understand or couldn't pronounce.

PART FIVE
JUNGLE BOUND

32

TIED IN THAILAND

There was a modicum of interest from inside the steel cage when they crossed the border into Thailand, recognisable by the change in lettering on the train stations. English, thanks to the British colonial influence in Singapore and Malaya, was replaced by Thai (Siamese) with Japanese subtitles. This put the men on edge. It registered a fear of the unknown, while at the same time creating some whispered talk about escape.

No one attempted to disabuse those contemplators of 'freedom'. The passing parade of impenetrable jungle and skyscraper-high, thick bamboo caused such rebellious thoughts to be submerged. At least on the ocean or on Java there was a sense that escaping to Australia was not an impossible dream. Not even the sudden appearance of rice fields in the valleys of mountains, with razor-back ridges, gave hope.

The high escarpments and sheer cliff faces caused one World War I veteran to cry out: 'Gallipoli!' His meaning was clear. This was tough country to negotiate.

Noel, the Tasmanian over-burdened with knowledge, announced to the carriage that this was rich country, in terms of food, compared to the ones they'd been through.

'Mangoes, apples, bananas—all kinds of fruit are here.'

'No rice?' Grout called out, and received a laugh.

'There's plenty of bamboo—'

'Lovely to eat, mate.'

'And maize and corn.'

'How do you know so much?' Grout asked.

'I think I'm autistic,' he told them all. Only Bolt had an idea of what he meant. 'It's a psychiatric condition discovered by a Swiss fellow, Eugen Bleuler.'

'It's akin to genius, right? You're probably a savant.'

'Could be, yes, but that's not proven.' The others were surprised by the revelation. 'Academics are sometimes autistic, at least a little.'

The others remained silent but intrigued. They'd always found diminutive Noel with the coke-bottle glasses somewhat different.

'Can you define it?' Bolt asked.

'No one can. In my case, I struggle to make friends, you know, communicate in social circumstances.'

Bolt waited.

'Go on, Leading Seaman. We are your friends.'

'I have repetitive behaviour.'

'Such as?'

'I check doors are locked over and over. I know I'm doing it but can't stop.'

'I've seen you playing with rope knots, tying them up, undoing them again,' Grout said, his tone sympathetic.

Noel nodded, and said, 'I'm told I often repeat myself and things I do.'

'But you do have a huge knowledge base in that brain of yours,' Bolt said. 'How come?'

'I don't know. All I know is that if I read something or see something I retain it forever.'

'A photographic memory?'

'Yeah, I guess. I thought it was normal for everyone as a kid. Then I realised my memory was extraordinary.'

'A gift, I would think,' Bolt said.

'Not sure.'

'It is, and you should see it that way.'

'How does it work when you read a book?' Bright asked. 'You've always got a book in your hands.'

'I can recall page numbers and everything on that page.'

'Everything?'

'Verbatim?' Bolt asked.

Noel nodded. 'I'm a hopeless writer, though. All that in my head and I can't express myself on paper.'

'Perhaps there's just too much in there,' Grout suggested, without attempting a joke.

'One doctor told my mother that I had more than the average number of brain orbits.'

No one knew what he meant but they left the conversation with more understanding than before for the odd little bloke. They also admired his courage in the face of some crudely cynical characters.

When Noel was not in earshot, Bright said to Bolt, 'He never has a bad word about anybody; he wouldn't hurt a fly.'

'I've observed him with Red Lead. They like each other. She draws out something like "feeling" in Noel. He pats her with affection.'

*

They reached their destination of Bampong, 35 miles west of Bangkok, after four days. It was not yet 7 a.m. on day five and still cold. The POWs stretched their legs, and were greeted by a collection of crowing, huge black birds—vultures—which none had seen before. The birds sat on tree branches overlooking the train platform, and mesmerised the apprehensive travellers. But the sight of food stalls near the station distracted them. The men bought ducks' eggs and wolfed them down. After the steady diet of rice, this was luxury.

There was no transport waiting for them. Farrow and Tait wandered a block and noticed a shabby temple. A few monks in saffron robes appeared and then disappeared in an eye blink. The Japanese offered the usual meal, but the men opted for bananas, if they had enough money, from another stall. Bolt was delighted when he sampled his first mango. It was fleshy and filling. He bought pumpkin for Red Lead, who was happy to slink about for a few minutes before peeing.

The Japanese, after some heated conversation about vehicles that had not arrived, broke it to the POWs that they would have to march from now on. This was not taken well by the men in general, but with rifles being waved at them and some quite vicious punches to backs and arms, they obeyed.

It took two days' hike by road and elephant tracks to cover the 20 miles to Kanchanaburi, enduring heavy thunder and rainstorms, which slowed progress for two hours. Most of the trek was at night to avoid detection by Allied planes. In the days, Bolt and his group rested and watched the Thais at work in their rural habitat. They controlled hundreds of ducks by flicking long bamboo sticks as if they were giant conductor's batons.

Red Lead, free and adventurous, began stalking a stray duck, only to be frightened off by a buffalo wallowing in a paddy-field bog.

Kanchanaburi village was a collection of bamboo and attap huts, and a few stores. It had a base camp on its outskirts marked by a bamboo fence perimeter. Japanese sentries manned lookout towers. They were alert. Tait guessed that there had been breakouts by members of previous POW gangs. The guards' slow, deliberate movements, and the occasional lifting of binoculars, backed up this suggestion.

Hoto made a surprise visit to their hut on the evening of the second day there and singled out Bolt.

'Tell all your countrymen that the guards will shoot to kill if you try to leave, or cause trouble,' he said with a cold smile. 'This town is in jungle. The nearest Allies are in India, about 1000 miles from here. The Thais are with us. They will inform us if any of you get out.'

'Hear they have been stealing from you as well as our boys,' Bolt said.

'They steal from everyone!' Hoto thundered, raising a threatening hand. Bolt noticed his gift from Pamela was around the sergeant's thick wrist, but said nothing. He also did not mention that the Thais were offering the POWs food purloined from the Japanese. The thieving had a quaint symmetry about it.

On the night of day three at Kanchanaburi, eight empty trucks rolled up driven by Thais. The men piled in and were driven on a dusty track to a bamboo bridge over a river that the drivers were reluctant to attempt to cross. The men were ordered out and marched across the bridge. The trucks then followed and the men embarked again.

The bumpy ride to a camp, Tarsau, that followed did not make the POWs any happier. Those with illnesses suffered. The fit men carried their mates' packs and aided them where they could but it was a demanding experience on top of the long train trip. Yet there was a reward of a river swim, which Red Lead enjoyed as much as any man. She refused to leave the water, from which she drank. Bolt was forced to dive in and retrieve her. She wailed in disappointment like a spoilt child, yet calmed down when offered pumpkin and a few cashew nuts. She took her time crunching through them, much to the surprise and amusement of Bolt and his group.

'She must need the fat, carbs and protein,' Noel said as he passed by, dripping wet. 'That's what cashews are.'

Red Lead enjoyed the rice and salt fish, dished out to everyone, that followed the swim. After that, the POWs slept where they dropped in makeshift bamboo huts. Bolt let the cat out and was thankful that she was not inclined to roam. It was a good sign. Perhaps she was now used to the moveable abode, even though it was not a cat's usual way. They often fretted over leaving a home. But Red Lead seemed adaptable.

Day five saw them all pushed into the trucks again and driven along elephant tracks that ended in a steep incline that a mountain goat may have baulked at. The truck drivers, all smiling Thais now, made the effort. The POWs had to alight once more and help push the vehicles up. After a few hours of this strenuous activity, the trucks were able, with a few worrying slips and slides, to negotiate the barely discernible tracks that led into mountains up to 1500 yards high.

The next stop was Wampo, 25 miles north-west. A rocky hillside fell sharply into the Maeklaung River (later named Kwai). They were informed by the Japanese that British, Dutch, Australians, Javanese, Tamils, Chinese, Malays and Thais had constructed a 120-yard triple-tier viaduct.

'Work of engineering art!' a proud Little Hitler told them.

They were moved on to the dusty, large Tarsau base camp, 7 miles north-west of Wampo, the third site on the planned new railway. They were only 600 yards from the river. The camp was typically primitive, with a handful of huts and stores for the camp administration and guards. Two flimsy huts were designated 'hospital huts'.

Bolt released Red Lead and surveyed the country beyond. It was steeper. Hills merged into mountains. The terrain was wild, rugged and covered in dense jungle. It was discouraging now for all the men, who were tired from the travel, even before they had started the heavy labour.

They were allowed to go to the river, which delighted Red Lead, Bolt and Tait, who could use the time to access the radio in his backpack. But the others hung back. They'd heard stories about the water being contaminated because of use by so many hundreds of POWs, and indigenous groups, who were not schooled in hygiene and in how to avoid diseases such as cholera. This disease was carried by faeces and transmitted by not washing hands thoroughly and drinking contaminated water.

Bolt, carrying a happily limp Red Lead, cajoled Tait and a few others into moving upstream about 500 yards from the camp for a swim. Red Lead splashed about, enjoying the chance. She ducked her head underwater for an alarmingly long time but always emerged calmly.

Tait took his radio out of his backpack and used the time to pick up anything he could.

'The Allies are stepping up their bombing of the railway,' he told Bolt as he towelled off. 'But the big news is that the Yanks have killed Yamamoto, the architect of the Pearl Harbor attacks.'

'Wow, that is big! The Japanese supreme naval commander!'

'Yank P-38s shot him down over Bougainville.'

'That will shake up the Nips, baby,' Bolt said, picking up a dripping Red Lead. 'Good news!'

A hastily built kitchen back at the camp served the usual, without the green streaks in the soup. It was after dark when the POWs bedded down, with the help of torches, for a long-awaited rest in a different and challenging topography.

33

KING COBRA CALAMITY

Bolt had just put a blanket over himself and the snuggling Red Lead when there was a shrill cry from someone a few yards away.

'Snake! Big snake!' Nadler screamed.

'Don't move!' Bolt said.

Too late. Growling like a wild dog, a long king cobra had bitten Nadler on the calf. It would not let go as it sank its fangs in. Red Lead flew at its throat and bit hard on the soft under-tissue and would not let go. She propelled her paws up and clawed at the reptile's eyes. The snake was so intent on the bite that it held on for up to 30 seconds, pumping poison into Nadler, despite Red Lead's attack, which had no impact.

Then the reptile let go, with the cat hanging on to its throat. The thick-bodied monster thrashed around, making nightmarish, guttural sounds. The violent movement flung Red Lead 5 yards away. She hit the base of a tree and seemed knocked out.

Several men moved to bash the cobra on the head with anything they could. Bolt swung an axe, which stuck in its neck. The reptile grunted. Its head fell to the ground, stunned but by no means finished. Grout swung a hammer at it, but only managed a glancing blow. Farrow pulled a burning log from the smouldering fire and swung it like a baseball bat as the cobra reared its head again. Bolt, Grout and Wallis followed with lumps of wood, bashing down on the thick skull. The axe wedged in the reptile's neck fell free. Bolt grabbed it and delivered six forceful blows to the base of the cobra's neck and head.

After at least another twenty blows from Bolt, Grout, Wallis and Farrow the monster's head stopped moving. Still the tail flicked and undulated, slapping legs standing close and creating slimy welts.

Nadler lay still. Bolt felt for a pulse. There was none. Bolt examined the calf and applied a tourniquet above it. He slapped Nadler and pumped his chest, but there was no saving him. Four men carried him to the hospital hut, where there was no medical aid.

A doctor from the 7th Division arrived and pronounced him dead.

'Takes about ten seconds depending on the dose,' the doctor said.

'I reckon the cobra pumped everything it had into poor Nadler,' Tait said.

The man had absorbed too much venom from the deadliest snake of all.

*

Attention turned to Red Lead. Bolt examined her.

'She okay?' a concerned Grout said.

'Dazed,' Bolt said, 'she has a bump on her skull.'

He carried her to the camp beds and laid her on a blanket. Bolt patted her, saying a few words of comfort. Her eyes opened and closed several times.

*

Even though Nadler was disliked by everyone, it was still a terrible blow. He was buried the next morning. Wallis, with whom he was partnered everywhere, said a few mumbled, incoherent words over the grave. He was stunned, but didn't appear deeply moved by Nadler's shocking end.

An investigation at the scene found that they had bedded down close to the cobra's nest in the nearby shrubbery. They found a dozen eggs and threw them on the fire.

'It's a shock,' Grout said, 'but I can't say I'll miss Nadler. He was a carping, bullying bastard.'

'Never speak ill of the dead,' Noel chanted six times, shaking his head.

'Why? I spoke ill of him while he was alive. What's the difference?'

Wallis, who would normally try to bully somebody, was too dispirited to defend his mate. He either didn't wish to, or could find no reason. Lethargy gripped him.

They had a post-mortem on the snake; its body was measured at 10 feet. Its flattened head was examined. On its crown was thick bone like armour-plating, and the telltale diamond-shaped marking. The body was dark grey with white rings. The underside was yellow. They had a close look at the bite marks on the small area of vulnerability on the throat where Red Lead had done no real damage, before the axe blows and bashings finished the reptile off.

All eyes turned to Red Lead. She was stretched out asleep on Bolt's backpack. Her mouth and nose twitched.

'She's having a nightmare,' Bolt observed. 'Still groggy from the blow last night. She needs rest. I think she'll be okay.'

'How did she know to go for the jugular like that?' Tait asked in awe.

'Watch any big cat,' Noel said. 'They all do.'

'Okay,' Farrow said, 'but there was no light. How did she zero in, in what, a split second?'

'I had my torch on the whole thing,' Grout said, in a serious tone few had heard much of. 'The cobra had sunk its fangs into Nadler's calf, maybe six inches off the ground, and was holding on. Red Lead speared under it and bit upwards at the precise second the cobra's head was steady. She gripped its face—its eyes—with her claws and just did not let go of the throat until forced to by the cobra.'

Bright was astonished.

'That cat is the sweetest, friendliest animal I've ever known,' he said. 'Even when Nadler, God rest his soul, stood in her path or kicked at her, she just sidestepped him with a sort of querulous expression. She kept out of his way but was never antagonistic.'

'The king cobra has enough venom to kill an elephant,' Noel remarked, 'or a cricket team.'

Everyone looked at Red Lead again.

'Is that the bravest living thing pound for pound, ever?' Tait said.

'Dunno about pound for pound,' Grout said. 'Just say *bravest living thing*. Full stop.'

They all mumbled their agreement, even Wallis.

Red Lead was still concussed the next day and took things quietly, lying on Bolt's blanket and sleeping.

*

About a hundred POWs, a mix of 7th Division gunners and sailors, including Bolt's group, were trucked another 15 miles up the line being constructed at Konyu. On the way, they learned what they were involved in with some more clarity. The railway would run from Bampong in Thailand through the border at a town called Three Pagodas Pass and deep into Burma. Work was already in steady progress from Bampong.

The men would be involved in a concentrated effort at Konyu to add to the railway line. First, they had to clear the place, which had already been done in part by earlier groups. Bolt and his group stripped to slouch hats—given to them by the gunners—shorts and boots. Some wore thick footy socks, as if that could help ward off any more reptiles in the vicinity. Everyone, including the others in the force, was made aware of Nadler's demise. All were more nervous than before, especially when clearing scrub.

'The Japs seem keen to break us up,' Farrow observed as he swung an axe into a tree.

'Divide and conquer, or at least keep us conquered,' Bright said, cutting down tall bamboo.

'Do you think they are worried we could rebel if in bigger teams?'

'Maybe, but we are early runners here. Who knows? I do sense there seems to be greater urgency every day.'

Tait was asked for his assessments. He still had his radio, hidden in the jungle everywhere he went. He was picking up broadcasts from the BBC, and Australia's ABC radio.

'I think the whole Pacific war is at a crossroads,' he said, perhaps with a little melodrama as the font of all knowledge on the world outside. 'The Japs have been having a real crack in Papua and New Guinea. They've sent about 250,000 soldiers there. They are lodged on the northern coast at places called Salamaua and Lae. Our blokes have held the line or pushed them back in three major, prolonged battles. The Nips can't get down to Moresby on the Kokoda Track.'

'We're not losing then?' Farrow asked.

'We only lose if they take Australia,' Bright chimed in.

'I don't think that's possible now,' Bolt noted. 'The Yanks are there in big numbers now.'

'That's right,' Tait confirmed. 'They are all over the place, according to the ABC reports; an estimated one million combat troops. They are calling Australia the Yanks' "floating aircraft carrier".'

That information lifted all their spirits. They all felt that there was now less chance of their fears being realised about the Japanese killing their families and raping their womenfolk. They'd heard terrible tales from the Chinese in Singapore, who claimed that the Japanese were continuing to pillage and rampage through eastern China.

Tait's analysis gave them fleeting good feelings. Meanwhile their small world appeared without hope in an unfamiliar, threatening wilderness. The danger came from their captors, unseen predators, natives that were not to be trusted and, worst of all, hideous diseases that were striking down men daily.

Dysentery was the ongoing scourge that could be handled, just. But many were succumbing to it and dying. The food was not nearly enough to build energy for hard labour. The Japanese attitude was that the weak should be fed less and left to die if they could not recover. Their rations should be given to those fit enough to carry on. If the numbers dwindled, the Japanese overlords were confident they could obtain more Asian workers from all over their conquered territory.

POWs in a close-by British camp were falling daily. In both sites men were suffering from ulcerated throats, mouths and tongues. Tinea was hitting in many parts of the body. All this in less than a week.

The Australians went to a lot of trouble to clear the area around the camp but they could not keep nature at bay. At night, they were in rough clearings some distance from trees and bush. The men wore as much clothing as possible and pulled blankets up over them under mosquito nets. One night when Bolt fell asleep with Red Lead stretched out beside him, making him feel protected, he was rudely awakened by Wallis yelling, 'Shit, shit, shit!'

'What?' others called.

'Snakes!'

Tait and Farrow shone torches just in time to see the last inches of a 4-foot snake slide over a petrified Wallis. Bolt grabbed Red Lead and restrained her.

'Don't move!' Bolt said.

Farrow picked up an axe that lay beside him and struck the snake, cutting it in half. Its front slithered on. Farrow stalked it and struck again, slicing into its neck with an indirect cut, which was enough to stun it to a stop. The stationary target was easier to hit. Farrow smashed the diamond-shaped head.

Everyone was awake now, examining the new intruder.

'It's a krait,' Noel opined. 'They also have plenty of poison. Didn't realise they were found outside India.'

Just at that moment, Red Lead, troubled by something near her, jumped a foot into the air and squealed. A torch was shone in her direction. It put the spotlight on a scorpion about 5 inches long with a tail that buzzed. Bolt brought a boot down on it. It seemed impervious. He smashed it again and again. It still squirmed. Bright came over with his axe and finished it off.

'Fuck me! What next?' someone said.

'How about a drink?' Grout asked, pulling a bottle of Thai whiskey from his pack. 'Got this today. Moonshine, no doubt, but still alcohol!'

34

A BELTING FOR
YOUR TROUBLE

Bolt awoke before everyone else at 7 a.m., put a towel over his shoulder and carried Red Lead several hundred yards to the river, well upstream from the camp. It was cold. Red Lead watched, reluctant to go in as Bolt eased himself under the water. He fought to breathe normally as he swam about 50 yards, and then back to Red Lead. She meowed as if she needed encouragement to join him. He splashed her. She jumped back, annoyed. Then she ran to the edge and fell in.

Bolt went for another quick sprint. When he returned Red Lead was already out of the water, shaking herself. He towelled her down and carried her back towards the camp. About 100 yards from it, she wriggled to be free. Bolt watched as she stalked something he could not see. He followed her. There was a green tree-snake curled up on the ground. The cat's belly was touching the grass as she prepared to pounce.

'Red Lead, no!' Bolt growled. Her pinned-back ears flicked. Then she sat up. The snake, sensing danger, uncurled and slithered up the nearest thick bamboo tree. Bolt dropped to his haunches and patted Red Lead softly. He waited for her to come down from the pre-attack tension, which included what could be construed as a 'dirty' look at him. Bolt scooped her up and carried her back to the camp.

*

At 8 a.m., after the most meagre rice serving on the 'trip' so far, the men were unhappy as they began the day's hard work under supervision from a dozen guards, including the strutting Little Hitler, who was the corporal in charge.

He delighted in slamming his rifle into Bolt and his mates, with whom he exhibited a strange sadistic attitude. Wallis was in no mood for the solid blow he received in the ribs. Before other guards could react, he had wrenched the rifle from Little Hitler and had thrown it over his head. In a tense moment, the other guards ran over and surrounded Wallis. Little Hitler, red-faced and hissing something vile, picked up his rifle and came close to Wallis. He ordered the guards to lay into him with rifles, fists and boots. The hundred or so POWs stopped their work and stood in disbelief.

'Hey, Corporal!' Bolt said, stepping near the brutality. 'That's enough!'

Little Hitler marched up to Bolt and swung the rifle at his chest. It brought him down. The action signalled the end of Wallis's bashing, but Bolt was kicked and hit as he curled into a fetal position.

The POWs were yelled at, and belted more with rifle butts.

'Work! Speedo! Speedo!'

Four guards carried the semi-conscious Wallis and helped Bolt to the open-roofed hospital. Wallis had a broken cheekbone and a fractured right forearm, as well as many marks on his body, including his genitals. Bolt had a six-inch welt across his chest that was already purple, and about ten bruises to the head, arms, legs and back.

Both men lay there dozing for about four hours, looking up at a multicoloured, mainly purple and green, jungle ridge. It had a yellow face, which reminded them of the Australian bush in winter. They were made alert by tropical rain crashing into the open hut. Bolt sat up gingerly. Wallis tried but could not do so without searing pain shooting through his big frame.

'I'll get a doctor, mate,' Bolt said. 'One of our blokes in the new batch from Changi that came in today.'

Bolt argued with the stubborn Little Hitler, saying he had to get a doctor. The corporal was adamant that Wallis should be left alone.

'You'll have a murder on your hands, Corporal, if he dies,' Bolt said.

'You don't go!' Little Hitler shouted, drawing a revolver from his belt.

'I have to go,' Bolt said, keeping his tone conciliatory. 'Otherwise that man will die.'

The POWs had stopped work again to watch the confrontation. Even the guards waited to see the outcome.

Bolt saluted, turned and began to walk towards the new camp about 200 yards down the track. The corporal took a few paces after him. He cocked his gun. Bolt froze at the sound and shut his eyes. After a few seconds, he moved on, leaving Little Hitler standing with the gun still aimed at Bolt's head. He then holstered the gun, turned and, to save face, began shouting orders at his guards and the POWs.

*

The 6 feet 4 inches tall, moustachioed Australian doctor examined Wallis for ten minutes. Looking on were Bolt, with a bandage across his chest, and Little Hitler. Red Lead wandered into the hut and jumped onto a stool. She looked around the room as if interested in everything.

'Sticky nose,' Bolt said, cuffing her gently under the chin.

'What a beautiful animal!' the doctor said, taking off his stethoscope. 'Such luxurious fur! A fellow surgeon in London had one just like that.'

The doctor scribbled a note and handed it to Little Hitler. 'I need those drugs,' the doctor said quietly to the corporal.

'No!' Little Hitler said. He stood defiantly in front of the doctor, who repeated the request.

'You know Commander Hiroshiga?' the doctor said with a respectful smile.

The corporal nodded.

'I treated him for an ulcer on his knee this morning,' the doctor added. 'He came to our camp as soon as I arrived. It was a very painful operation. Your commander is very brave. We used that drug.' He pointed to the paper in Little Hitler's hand. 'It's in store now. I brought it with me.'

The corporal still looked defiant. 'No!'

'Get it, or I shall report you to the commander,' the doctor said, his manner changing.

'No.'

'I need it now.'

Little Hitler had half-mouthed 'no' again, when the doctor struck him hard with a clenched fist to the chest, then a round arm smack to the head. The big Japanese man went down. The doctor stood over him. A startled Red Lead scampered out of the hut.

'Get that drug!'

Little Hitler got to his feet and scrambled out, holding his head.

'There may be repercussions for that,' Bolt warned.

'No there won't,' the doctor said, resuming his under-stated, ultra-calm demeanour. 'They beat me up a couple of times, but not out here in the wilderness. All their officers come to us, rather than their own medicos.'

The doctor returned to his camp, telling Bolt to send for him when the drugs arrived. Bolt reported the stunning scenario to the rest of his group and Noel, who had insinuated himself into their midst. They were the only ones who would tolerate his interminable, encyclopaedic outbursts.

'Do you know who that was?' Noel asked in awe.

'No.'

'That was the CO of 7th Division, Weary Dunlop!'

'I had no idea,' Bolt said. 'I'd heard about him but never laid eyes on him. Played rugby for Australia, didn't he? How did he become CO as a medico?'

'Not sure,' Noel said. 'But I do know that every digger in the gunners swears by him. Oh, and he has a reputation as a boxer as well.'

'It makes sense that he's in charge, when you think of it,' Bolt said. 'There is no fighting here, except against disease, and who better than a man like Dunlop to command.' He paused and added, 'He just belted Little Hitler as if he was in the ring. Put him hard on his derrière. Wonderful, but perhaps too gutsy.'

'Good thing!' Bright said.

Bolt shook his head and said, 'Wonder how that will go down with the Jap officers.'

35

TIGER TIME

Little Hitler was given two weeks' solitary confinement at Konyu camp for his initial refusal to deliver much-needed drugs to Dunlop. It took that long for the battered Wallis to recover. He joined the number who were too ill to work. The slave force was down to only 12 per cent fit and able among the British, and 40 per cent among the Australians.

After three weeks at Konyu clearing and preparing for railway sleepers to be laid, the disparate group—including sailors, gunners, British soldiers and a small band of 30 Dutch—were moved further up the River Maeklaung (Kwai), where other POWs had constructed two bridges. One was a temporary wooden trestle span built to allow construction traffic to cross the river. This facilitated a second bridge of steel and concrete to be put up in just three months, using manpower, a few pulleys, derricks and cement mixers.

The 300 new arrivals stopped at Tamarkan camp on the river's east bank, about 170 yards from the bridge.

'You've got to admire this country,' Bolt said to the others as they sat by the bank with Red Lead.

'Yeah, bloody Jap and Korean psychopath guards and unfriendly natives!' Farrow said.

'I'm talking about the country, the feel of the place.'

'It's Buddhist. They are a calm lot,' Noel said.

'They sided with the fuckin' Nips,' Wallis said. 'Gutless!'

'Not all of them,' Noel said. 'The Thais in the north fought the good fight.'

'Not for long,' Wallis grunted.

'They're attractive people,' Bolt said. 'They're spiritual. They have sold us a lot of food and other things. The Japs are tough on them when they find out.'

'They say they've been press-ganged into work, like us,' Noel proffered, 'but the Nips are much tougher on them. The locals say many thousands of them have died already.'

'Bullshit! Don't trust any of them,' Wallis added.

'I think some of the women are the most serene and beautiful I have seen,' Bolt said, absent-mindedly.

'The sun has got to you,' Wallis mumbled.

'No,' Grout said, 'Dan hasn't been to the African Congo and seen the midgets.'

The others laughed.

'They're not all midgets,' Noel said and was howled down by the others.

They heard several high-pitched cries.

'What's that? Baboons?' Farrow asked.

'No, monkeys,' Noel informed them. 'They sound like birds sometimes. But you rarely see the birds. They keep high in the trees, except the herons and geese on the river.'

'Bad luck, eh, Red Lead?' Grout said. 'Too high for you?'

The cat meowed at the mention of her name.

'I wouldn't bet on that,' Bolt said. He pointed to a mango grove next to a clump of banana trees. 'Let's sample some of the fruit here.'

*

Later the Allied slave gang was moved on, this time on foot, heading north for Hintok camp. The last 2 miles of the trek passed through the already notorious Hellfire Pass. They reached the pass just after dark, and looked down at Australians working there by candlelight. They were cutting rock.

'The jaws of hell,' Farrow noted, sadly.

After a day's trudge, the Japanese guards, including Little Hitler, ordered them to make big fires at their stop by the river for the night.

'This tiger country,' he said with a pretend look of concern.

'He's trying to scare us,' Wallis grumbled.

'He's succeeded,' Grout said with a shudder.

'It *is* tiger country,' Noel confirmed. 'The native I bought coconuts from warned me too.'

'Better make it a bonfire,' Grout said.

Many of the POWs slept with their work implements—shovels, axes and hammers—close by.

*

They were bedded down by 10 p.m. close to a fire, which blazed enough for the men to feel warm and safe in the open. However, Red Lead was restless.

'Something out there is bothering her,' Bolt said as he lay awake. He tried to ease his mind by working out which stars were which, but dared not ask Noel, who would know and keep everyone awake with a celestial lecture. After an hour Bolt was dozing off when Red Lead stood and arched her back. She took a few cautious steps to the left of the fire and then moved in front of it. Grout noticed and nudged Bolt awake.

'She's spotted something,' he whispered.

'Locals?'

'No, not here.'

They were both startled by a loud growl, then another, and a third in the distance.

'Those are tigers,' Bolt said, his voice low. 'I'd say they were no more than two hundred yards from here.'

Everyone in the group was woken by the sound. Red Lead, meanwhile, had crept in pre-attack mode about 10 yards in front of the fire. The tigers' roars came closer. All the men were sitting and alert.

Then they saw a huge tiger standing in a clearing not 20 yards from the fire.

'No, Red Lead!' Bolt called as the small cat slipped closer to the big one. Red Lead charged. The big cat, momentarily startled, turned and moved away a few paces. Then it spotted Red Lead sprint by and up a tree. The men stood, transfixed at what they were witnessing.

Red Lead ran across a tree branch, which was about 6 feet above the tiger's head. The big cat realised that its tormentor was a pint-sized version of itself. The tiger jumped up, swinging a paw at Red Lead, which hit the tree branch. Red Lead had to balance adroitly to stop from toppling to the ground. As the tiger roared and steadied itself for another swipe, Red Lead dashed to the trunk and clawed higher and out of reach. The tiger leapt higher this time, but well short of Red Lead.

The men all gripped weapons of some sort. Farrow ran a few paces forward and launched a hammer at the tiger. It hit the animal on the rump, causing a yelp, then a roar of defiance.

'Jesus!' Noel cried. 'Don't antagonise the bugger!'

The men stayed close to the fire. Japanese guards appeared, rifles at the ready. One propped, fired and missed from 40 yards. The tiger turned at the sound of the shot and took a few paces in the guard's direction. The man dropped his rifle and ran. That caused two others to turn and follow, knees up and screaming.

'So much for dying for the bloody emperor!' Grout remarked, causing a titter of nervous laughter from those who heard him.

Bolt was concerned about Red Lead, who the tiger had not forgotten. The big cat circled the tree, growling in a blood-tingling manner for everyone near and far. It sat at the base of the tree as if ready to spring. Torchlights picked the animal up, its black and yellow stripes evident. The tiger was still for a few seconds, apparently making up its mind if the small cat was worth the effort. Bolt crept forward five paces in front of the fire and hurled a short axe. It spun like a tomahawk and struck the tiger in the side. It roared and raced off into the jungle.

No one ventured away from the fire. Torches were trained on the area in which the tiger had been. After about ten minutes Red Lead careered down the tree trunk and back to the campfire. Bolt and the others patted her. Her little heart was pounding almost in sync with a purr that became louder.

Everyone told her how brave she was, except Grout.

'Nar,' he said with a mock shake of his head, 'she can't even take on a little scorpion!'

No one could return to bed. They chatted in awed tones about the tiger's size.

'Never seen one like that at the Sydney zoo,' Wallis said. 'Massive, like a bull!'

'I quite liked it,' Grout said, causing everyone to glance at him. 'It had the right colours, didn't it?'

36

CHOLERA STRIKES

Over the next month, more and more emaciated corpses were seen lying outside huts in the early morning after doctors had made their inspections. Farrow caught malaria and began to waste away. One day, at a camp they'd just moved to called Lower Nieke, a doctor, Frank Cahill, shook Farrow hard, but he did not respond. Bolt was lying a few feet away. Cahill slapped Farrow hard on both cheeks. Farrow stirred, opened his eyes and said, 'Morning, Doc, Dan. Sorry, fellas, not this morning. Perhaps another time.'

Cahill walked outside with Bolt. They'd known each other from university days.

'Terrible business, these inspections,' Cahill said, 'they always know what I'm doing. So many blokes have malaria.' He pointed to three bodies outside a hut 40 yards away. 'I hate this part of the job. We can't do anything. Those men are an awful sight; bones protruding; eyes open and staring.

I never know sometimes if they are gone or not. Most, like Farrow, are just a heartbeat away from their maker.'

They watched as orderlies placed the three bodies on stretchers made of bamboo poles pushed through a sack. The corpses' heads, legs and arms hung loosely and swung to the movement of the carriers as they took the bodies to the cemetery.

'Not the crematorium for those blokes?' Bolt asked as he felt Red Lead brushing against his legs.

'We only burn the most dangerous ones, like those with cholera,' the doctor said matter-of-factly. 'The Poms pour formaldehyde on them. Doesn't quite do the trick. The disease remains. We put them on a funeral pyre.'

'You reckon we'll get cholera here?'

'Inevitable. The coolies—Javanese, Tamils, Chinese, Burmese and Thais—are living in absolute filth and squalor at this camp. Your huts have no covering.'

'I know cats can't get it,' Bolt said, cuddling Red Lead.

'No. Apart from the nine lives nonsense, these wonderful creatures are very disease resistant, usually.' He paused to pat Red Lead. 'I heard what this little blighter did to a king cobra. Amazing!'

'Don't forget the tiger.'

'Oh yeah! That story gets bigger every day. Bet you're happy to be clear of that country. There are no tigers around these parts.'

The doctor was about to move on, when he stopped.

'Dan,' he said, dropping his voice, 'we know there are a couple of cholera cases among the coolies a few miles from here. We're trying to contain it with extreme hygiene methods. But it's only a matter of time. I'm in charge until

Doctor Bruce Hunt arrives. I won't let our blokes work until the camps are cleaned up. Hunt has a reputation that rhymes with his name. He's brutal in keeping people alive. Different from Dunlop but just as gutsy and effective.'

'I see you've had slit trenches built for toilets,' Bolt said. 'Thanks for that and the water points.'

'That's okay. Tell your men to make sure they understand one is for washing after working. The other, with boiling water, is for them to drink.'

'They are already well aware.'

'Good. We can beat it, or at least contain it with serious health standards.' He added as an afterthought, 'I know you like to go swimming in the rivers. Don't!'

*

The men were put to work on bridge and road construction. First, tracks had to be cleared using limited billhooks, axes, saws and rope. It took Bolt and his group, minus the ill Farrow and Wallis with his broken forearm, and fourteen others a full day to remove a big clump of bamboo.

Word soon swept through the camps that cholera had struck. There was panic among the Japanese, as one of their own, Sergeant Hoto, had caught it. He was transferred to a special set of tents on a small mound, which was soon known as Cholera Hill. Within 48 hours there were twelve cases, including six diggers. Doctor Bruce Hunt, a former artillery officer under General Monash in World War I, arrived to take charge. He had all the camps scrubbed but he could not keep pace with the pestilence. It hit 35 Australians early one morning. They lost half their bodyweight within twelve hours and many were dead by nightfall. The medical staff was too small to supply adequate nursing to these men. The evening after the disease struck, Hunt and Cahill met the Australians, including Bolt and his group, who had been working for fourteen hours in the monsoon rains knee-deep in mud. Hunt explained the situation. He wanted volunteers to nurse the sick.

'The mortality rate for cholera is fifty per cent,' he said. 'Every second patient you nurse will die.' He paused in front of the men, walked a few paces closer to them and added: 'I want you now—right now! Straightaway! Hands up those who'll do it. We need seventy-five men.'

Bolt felt that his vet background obligated him to volunteer. He raised his hand and looked around. There were about 100 hands up. Others followed. Hunt and Cahill began counting. They stopped at 120. Hunt was overwhelmed. He turned to Cahill, and, dropping his voice, said with emotion, 'This response makes me very proud to be an Australian.'

37

GOOD DOCTOR VET

Bolt, the vet school drop-out, found himself face to face
with Sergeant Hoto on Cholera Hill. The Japanese officer,
who had displayed so much fickle and at times vicious
behaviour in front of the POWs, was now at the mercy of
the Australian. Bolt nodded curtly to him without a word
and injected him with morphine, which put him out to it
quickly. Bolt was appalled at Hoto's condition. His once
short but muscular legs had wasted inside a day. His face
was hollow like a dying nonagenarian. His sloping forehead
had disappeared. The top of his skull was now almost
linked to his eyebrow ridge. His head had shrunk to half
its normal size. The gold watch that Bolt had bribed him
with now looked more like a loose bracelet hanging from
his withered wrist.

The Allied doctors had been calling instructions from
30 yards away to the scores of volunteers on duty in the middle
of the night. None of the doctors, including the sensitive,

gifted and dedicated Frank Cahill, would go near the cholera tents. As Hunt in his sharp manner had said, 'We are much better off alive, for the good of all the POWs.'

This implied that Bolt and the other novice nurses were all expendable. Bolt, who'd done enough practical work with animals, was the one all the others looked to for help. The doctors were helpful, but Bolt was right there among the sick. He cleaned a scalpel and held it up under torch-light for all to see. Then, with the spotlight following his hand, he made an incision into Hoto's ankle. This exposed a large vein. It was a good surgical cut and only a fine trickle of blood was released, where a bad cut could cause a messy ooze. Next, he inserted a bamboo tube into the vein. Saline was pumped into the patient. That was it. Bolt then super-vised every other volunteer as they made the cuts. Some got it right; others were shaking so much that they lacerated the patient and Bolt had to take over.

There were 30 patients left alive by the morning, when an exhausted Bolt dragged himself out of the tent. He washed thoroughly and moved to his hut. Red Lead was there, waiting. She stood to greet him. He fell asleep in the only place he could find in a room crowded with snoring, sweating men. There was no special boudoir for a man who had just helped keep alive so many of his countrymen and one enemy soldier, whom he did not care for. Red Lead snuggled at his feet under a blanket.

The next morning before dawn he was awakened rudely by a Japanese officer, who nevertheless was deferential, address-ing him as 'Doctor, sir'. Bolt pulled on footy shorts and boots and followed the officer to a hut 100 yards from the others. There were two other Japanese patients in it. There was no doubt in his mind that they were severe cholera victims. Bolt examined them. Both were nearly dead, he advised the officer and two guards, who stayed 40 yards away.

'Please, help them, if you can,' the nervous officer said in clear English.

There were surgical implements and a saline drip close by. The Japanese soldiers set it up for him, but none of their doctors would come near the place. Bolt sighed to himself and went through the ritual of the incision and insertion. After about half an hour, he examined their pulses, which were non-existent. He went outside, told the officer and asked for matches.

'What for?' the officer asked, fumbling for matches and handing them over.

'Must burn the hut,' Bolt said and, without looking for the officer's reaction, he set about torching the small bamboo building, which was soon ablaze. He walked outside. The officer and the guards were making themselves scarce.

'Thank you, Doctor, sir,' the officer called, 'thank you, sir.'

*

Bolt felt a strange sense of satisfaction at the night's experience. It was a few years since he'd given up his vet studies, and he felt much more comfortable about this, or any kind of medical work, than ever before. It crossed his mind that he might just be ready to finish that degree, if he ever made it out of the war. He laughed cynically to himself. This unexpected new confidence had come straight after losing two patients.

He managed a few more hours' sleep before Cahill and Hunt summoned him for a conference. They wanted him to check on all the patients in Cholera Hill and report back to them. Bolt walked to the hill, a pep in his step. He entered the tent and any exuberance was sapped from him. Seven men were dead. He called for stretchers. Twenty-three were alive, five only just.

Hoto had somehow survived. He clutched Bolt's forearm with the force of a baby and pushed the gold watch into his hand.

Bolt hesitated, then pocketed it.

'Can . . . you save . . . me?' Hoto whispered so hoarsely and softly that Bolt had to put his ear close to the sergeant's mouth and ask him to repeat his words.

'I do anything for you . . .'

'Send me home to Australia?' Bolt asked, paused and added, 'Alive?'

Hoto blinked.

'I am doing what I can,' Bolt said. 'It may not be enough.'

He could not rid his mind of the massacre of the beautiful Javanese lighthouse family. He stared at the Japanese man for whom he had thoughts a long way beyond contempt. He glanced at the saline bag. Hoto's eyes did the same. They may both have had the same idea. One quick flick by Bolt would end this patient's life within minutes. There were only Australian nurses and patients in the Cholera Hill tent. No one would know; no one certainly would care.

Bolt had been under orders, passed on by Japanese officers, to attend to the Japanese patients first. One was already dead.

Bolt was effectively in charge. He had begun to accept the fact that he was 'expendable', even cheerfully. He felt he had a purpose: to save lives. So far, his score was not encouraging but handling cholera was the most difficult of situations. In addition, Bolt had not been able to save Nadler, although even Weary Dunlop had said no one could have defeated the lightning action of a king cobra's venom. Still, Bolt had mulled over whether or not he could have opened up and sucked into Nadler's calf to extract the poison. Dunlop had said, 'No, that would have killed you both. Your lovely king cobra was no ordinary carpet reptile.'

Bolt moved from patient to patient; he was beckoned all over the tent to every bed. Grout, who had also volunteered, insisted Bolt look at a man who was slipping fast. He didn't seem to have a pulse. Bolt checked it with a stethoscope Cahill had placed around his neck like a medallion.

'Something there . . .' Bolt whispered.

He thumped the victim's chest, attempting to get his slipping heart to start moving blood through the near-lifeless body.

At that moment an elephant wandered past the hut only a few yards from them.

'Jesus, Dan!' Grout said in disbelief. 'Look at that!'

Bolt kept pumping the man's heart as the elephant moved out with a modest trumpet, as if to register he'd won a bet with members of his herd.

'Bloody Thailand,' Grout grumbled, 'cobras one day; elephants the next.'

Bolt used the stethoscope again.

'He has a weak pulse. If only we had oxygen.'

Just then, Red Lead leapt onto the makeshift bed, purring. She nestled close to the man's side.

Grout moved to put her off the bed.

'No, leave her there,' Bolt said. 'You keep pumping the way I did.'

Bolt moved to another bed, then another. One dying digger had the strength to pull him close and say with cold clarity, 'I am going to see Mum.'

'Yep. Give her my regards,' was all Bolt could think to say as he loosened the grip on his shirt.

Another victim attracted his attention. 'My best mate has come to visit,' the man said, trying to sit up. He pointed at another patient in the corner of the room. 'We're going away together in his car.'

'Sure, friend,' Bolt said and walked to the 'mate'. He was dead.

Bolt and the other volunteer nurses began to ask each patient if they would like to hear the Lord's Prayer. No one rejected the quickly mumbled version.

Ambulance man Rex Fullerton whispered, 'I feel as if there is a monster in the room.'

Bolt nodded.

'It's a ghost. A killer ghost.'

He attended a man who was doubled up with cramps and crying in agony. On a bed close by, a soldier was begging for water with a rasping voice. Three yards away a victim's skin had turned blue-grey. His eyeballs were sunken. Bolt pointed a finger at the nurse nearby and shook his head. 'Get him out.'

Bolt then trotted with two stretcher-bearers to Cahill for a quick consultation.

'There's a young lieutenant who has just been brought in,' Bolt said. 'He has cholera. That might not kill him but he has an abscess on his back the size of a dinner plate. I fear it's septicaemic. I've handled this with dogs and horses, but not a human. Same method?'

'Yes, yes,' Cahill said, rummaging in a pack. 'Use this scalpel. It's sterilised. Cut both ankles and put the tubes in them.' Cahill handed him a second scalpel.

'Push it into the abscess?' Bolt said.

Cahill nodded. 'Scrape the whole dinner plate! Don't worry about the blood. Get the poison out of him.' Cahill pulled out a small bottle of pills. 'This is sulphanilamide. Get him to swallow four. If it's difficult, do what you do with a horse. Shove it into his throat and make sure it goes down.'

Bolt trotted back to the tent. He was concentrating on the lieutenant but noticed Red Lead. She had leapt onto Hoto's bed. She had her paws on his chest and was kneading him. Hoto had a feeble hand on the cat's back.

Bolt called for assistance. Two nurses, including Peter Chitty, turned the young lieutenant onto his front. Bolt directed Chitty and Fullerton to cut the ankles and insert the bamboo tubes. Bolt cut the abscess into triangular slices as if it were a pizza. The smell was horrific.

'Aw, Doc!' Fullerton said, coughing and just managing to stop from vomiting.

Bolt threw the pieces of abscess on the floor. There was blood but not as much as he expected.

'We need a dressing!' Bolt said, the first sign of anxiety in his voice.

'We don't bloody have any, Doc.'

'See Frank Cahill. Run!'

Fullerton did as instructed, and returned in a minute with two large bandages and a small, sterilised brush.

'Pour boiled water on it,' Bolt said to Chitty, pointing at the abscess crater. Chitty dribbled out the bottled, steaming water carefully. It sizzled on the flesh. Bolt used the brush to push out the remains of the abscess. Chitty kept a steady trickle of water coming. The patient shook a couple of times. When the crater was clear of dead tissue, Bolt applied the bandages.

'You've done this before, Doc,' Chitty said.

'On animals, yes,' Bolt said. He glanced over at Red Lead. She had stopped her massage of Hoto's chest. She was sitting close to his side, looking at his face.

Bolt took a break and walked outside with Fullerton. Another nurse offered them cigarettes. Bolt took one.

'I don't smoke,' he said, 'but I need something, anything right now.'

'You are doing well, Doc,' Fullerton said.

'Thanks. I'm not a doctor.'

Fullerton was surprised but said nothing, assuming that Bolt had to be a *real* nurse or some sort of trained medico.

Bolt strolled to Cahill. 'Two more dead,' he said.

'The lieutenant?'

'Don't know if he'll make it. We've done all we could.'

Red Lead wandered from the tent and moved with a little less than her usual swagger to them.

Bolt stubbed his cigarette with his boot and walked back to the tent. He examined Hoto.

He was dead.

38

MURDER AT THREE PAGODAS PASS

The young lieutenant died a few days later, and Bolt felt a deep sense of failure, even remorse. Yet he had helped save the lives of twenty-five men on Cholera Hill. Most importantly, the killer disease had been halted from taking over the entire camps around Nieke, Upper Konkoita and Songkurai, all at the upper end of the railway inside Thailand. Funeral pyres at the Australian camps were testimony to the battle with the worst problem, next to the slower, more insidious malaria, for all the slaves on the railway project.

Bolt was walking around Nieke for the last time with Cahill and an Australian captain from 7th Division. They passed a big pyre where about 30 bodies had been deposited in the final hours of the day as the camp packed up and prepared for a march further up the line.

'Never seen anything more macabre at night,' the captain said, waving a dismissive hand at the roaring flames being stoked by POWs. They could feel the heat from 20 yards, which was not unpleasant as the cold night set in.

'My God!' Cahill exclaimed and pointed at a body sitting up. One of its arms, then a leg appeared to salute them. 'He is waving to us!'

'Contraction of the tendons,' Bolt said, 'I've had to destroy horses and dispose of the carcasses by fire. Had them kick hard at me as if I'd done the wrong thing.'

The captain shuddered.

'I'm going to have nightmares forever!' he said.

'We all will,' Cahill said with a sad look. 'I'm already having them.'

'Have you ever thought why some of the POWs don't pick up the cholera when we've all been so exposed to it?'

'I have,' Cahill replied. 'There must be something in our genetic make-up, bearing in mind we might be struck down any moment. But that aside, history has shown during plagues, for instance, that some survive, some don't. It's a mystery that medical science will solve, one day.'

The 'Last Post' was played by a lone bugler 50 yards away. They were hearing it several times a day. The three men bowed their heads until the croaky, off-key rendition was over.

'That sounded a bit different,' the captain said. 'Not so melodic.'

'No,' Cahill agreed, 'the regular chap died this morning.'

*

The slave caravan marched on for two days to the last camp on the railway inside Thailand, just short of the town of Three Pagodas Pass. It sat at the foot of mountains which surrounded the town on the border with Burma.

Their camp was a few hundred yards from the Song Kalia River. Bolt wanted to take Red Lead for a swim, but seeing the black, brown and stinking cesspool of 4-feet-deep slit-trench toilets between the camp and the river, he decided instead on a run before dark.

The area was tranquil and pleasant with fine views along the river, which was more like a series of lakes. After undoing their packs and settling in a cleared area, Bolt and Grout shared some tea while admiring the view.

'There must be a hundred shades of green in the flora,' Bolt observed, indicating the riverbanks. 'Quite beautiful.'

'Good place for a holiday resort,' Grout responded, deadpan.

'At least it gives us a timeless antidote to the hell in the camps.'

The POWs had a fraction more freedom and were able to buy or purloin a few vegetables from stalls in the local village. They chopped up the much-sought-after food and added it to their rice. The men took their time eating around a campfire, relieved to be 40 miles from the cholera camp and about 70 miles from the thick jungle of tiger country and intense snake infestation.

'The pass has historic importance,' Noel told the group, who rolled their eyes at yet another tutorial. 'The Burmese have used it for invasions of the Lana Kingdom.'

'The what?' asked Farrow, who was making a slow recovery from malaria.

'Lana Kingdom. That was what the area was called.'

'Who gives a shit?' Wallis said, admiring himself in a cracked mirror and slicking his hair back with water.

He gave his dirty white boots a flick with a rag, and pulled up his football socks.

'Burmese have been invading Thailand since 1548,' Noel added, unfazed by the interruption.

'Geez, way back then,' Grout said. 'I think St Kilda won the flag that year.'

Wallis stood and straightened his tatty shirt. He made a play of tearing off his arm plaster. He flexed his forearm.

'Don't need this anymore,' he said.

'Where you goin'?' Tait asked.

'Mind your own business,' Wallis said. 'I spotted a sexy little number in them food stalls near those pathetic pagodas. I reckon she fancies me.'

'Be a little cautious, mate,' Bolt warned. 'If there are prostitutes there, the Japs are sure to know about them. Especially that close friend of yours, Little Hitler.'

'I'll deal with that turd if he gets in my way again,' Wallis said as he walked away.

'Turdus Maximus,' Grout called.

Wallis stopped, turned and asked menacingly, 'What did you call me?'

'Not you, Little Hitler.'

Wallis scrutinised Grout for a moment and muttered, 'You'll keep,' before disappearing into the night.

*

Wallis arrived at the grass square at 9 p.m., well after prisoner curfew. He stood nervously near the uninspiring three small cement-plaster pagodas, from which the town took its name. Wallis could see the red dot on a truck, lights on, heading along the track from the camp. There was a sudden monsoonal downpour. He moved to shelter near one of the closing stalls and noticed the young girl with jet-black long hair, with whom he thought he'd made a date. She was closing the stall of local artefacts.

Wallis took an American ten-dollar note and pushed it into her hand.

'Quick,' he said, 'Japs come!'

She protested. Wallis, twice her size, dragged her through a door into a small bamboo storeroom at the back of the stall. He put a hand over her mouth. They could see through the slats. Four Japanese, led by the arrogant Little Hitler, alighted from the truck.

The girl let go a stifled scream. Wallis belted her across the mouth. The Japanese didn't hear. They hustled to a hut on the other side of the square.

Wallis wanted his money's worth, but the girl was not receptive. She threw the money on the floor and wiped away a trickle of blood from her mouth.

'I tell Japanese!' she yelled at him, 'I tell Japanese!'

He pulled her to him, but she kicked and scratched. He pushed her away and there was a stand-off as she hurled abuse in Thai at him. She spat.

'Wild cat, eh? Like to play rough.'

He pushed her to the ground and fell on top of her. She wriggled free and grabbed a loose bamboo pole. She aimed it like a spear. He laughed gruffly and glanced through the bamboo slats again. She took the moment to dash to the stall and into the square, screaming all the way to the house where the Japanese were. Little Hitler came into the square doing up his trousers. He hurried, rifle in hand, to the stall where the girl was pointing.

Wallis made a run for the road. The four Japanese jumped in the truck and gave chase. They put their lights on high-beam and spotted him close to the water's edge. Three of them jumped from the truck and cornered Wallis, who put up his hands.

'Okay. Don't shoot,' Wallis said. 'Just having a little fun like you blokes were.'

'You!' Little Hitler said, walking a few yards from Wallis who was right on the water's edge. 'You get me into big trouble!'

He took a step closer, with the spotlight right on the cowering Wallis. Little Hitler pulled out his revolver and shot Wallis in the side of head. He stumbled and fell flat. Little Hitler stepped up close and fired into the back of Wallis's head. The four Japanese pushed the big body into the river, making sure it was submerged.

39

BODY OF EVIDENCE

The body of Able Seaman Warwick Oscar Wallis may never have been found except for Bolt's fitness fanaticism. He was on a 6 a.m. jog around the perimeter of the POW camp an hour before reveille, when the men had to fall in on parade. The work was back-breaking enough for most, but Bolt had a different mentality. He believed that the fitter and stronger he was, the better he would cope and also ward off the diseases that were felling his fellow POWs daily. Bolt now thought it unwise to swim. Exercise routines were fine, but the aerobic winner for him was a daily 5-mile jog. Most regarded him as the fittest of all the Australian POWs, next to the freak Peter Chitty, who had actually put on weight, perhaps the only prisoner to do so, in the twenty months of captivity.

Bolt didn't push himself. He did not wish to be exhausted during the railway work. The jog toned him up and prepared him for the heavy lifting, cutting, sawing and carrying.

The slow running pace allowed him to observe his surroundings in the sky, the bush and on the river, where fishermen were discernible as not much more than silhouettes in the early dawn and sunshine. Then he saw what he thought was just a boot. It was big and white. Bolt had a succession of quick thoughts. Wallis had gone out the night before but had not come back to their hut. That didn't mean he wasn't back in camp. But he'd been wearing white boots. Bolt clambered down an embankment. As he got closer, he could see a Geelong football club blue and white sock with its circular hoops. Then he discerned a leg with tatts and the word 'Mum'.

Bolt stood staring down into the river. He was looking at a dead body.

It was that of Warwick Oscar Wallis.

*

Bolt asked Frank Cahill to do an autopsy on Wallis, and a report was made. In the early afternoon, Wallis was buried in a growing graveyard at the entrance to the camp, which reminded everyone of the carnage everywhere on the railway.

Grout said a few words, keeping his eulogy general and not personal, except for one comment: 'No one would accuse Wally of being a good bloke, but he was okay, especially when asleep, when he snored a lot after his usual night of whoring and on the piss.' Grout looked around at the surprised mourners. 'Sorry,' he said, 'but it's the truth, which any man deserves at this moment.'

'Good thing the padre didn't hear that,' Farrow said, 'he's away burying more worthy souls.'

When the service ended Noel said to Grout and Farrow, 'I've never heard a sermon like that, ever.'

'I've heard worse,' Farrow said. 'Once I went to the funeral of the mother of a schoolmate. She had three sons. The first two made respectful comments. The third took the microphone and rounded on the casket with his mum in it. Said some awful things about her neglect of him.'

'Geez,' Grout said, 'I was a bit soft on Wally then, wasn't I?'

*

In the eyes of Japanese officers, even the murder of a lowly foreign POW had to be investigated. It was a serious business, especially as the Japanese might have been starting to realise that their mighty marauding empire could actually lose this war. With their Axis partners in Germany and Italy struggling, and Japan's battles in China in stalemate, it was filtering down to officers that they perhaps should be more circumspect in handling certain issues; for instance, the ill-treatment of their prisoners.

There was an investigation into Wallis's demise, carried out by a diligent, thorough Japanese lieutenant. Bolt and his group took it upon themselves to ask questions in Three Pagodas Pass village. Apart from attempted rape allegations against Wallis, there were witnesses who had seen a large Japanese corporal—Little Hitler—and three other guards give chase, waving their weapons.

This and the fact that Wallis had two bullets in his head was taken, in written submissions only, into the inquiry. After a few days, the Japanese lieutenant informed the

Australian commanding officers that there wasn't sufficient evidence to charge anyone.

Bolt and the others were incensed. In the few days during the probe, Little Hitler had made certain innuendoes about what would happen if they put forward any facts. He knew about the written evidence they'd presented.

The taciturn Farrow made one remark that turned Little Hitler's face purple. 'We know that you murdered the lighthouse keeper's family!'

The corporal took his sword from its scabbard, slowly, menacingly. He put it back in place and stormed off. Perhaps he realised there could be repercussions while the inquiry was ongoing, even from his superiors, who, after all, had acted against him when Weary Dunlop flattened him.

Little Hitler remained mute also when Grout made a sweeping motion across his own throat in full view of the corporal.

Two nights after the finding, which cleared Little Hitler, he and three guards forced their way into the group's hut and began swinging their rifles around, bashing everyone. Weapons were trained on the POWs, making it impossible to fight back. The thugs left after twenty minutes of brutality. Bolt received a bruised eye socket. Farrow had a broken rib. Grout had a bruised thigh. Tait had two fingers broken. Noel, ever the innocent party, had a lacerated scalp and a badly bruised back. Bright was effectively 'knee-capped', mafia-style, with rifle-butt smashes.

Only Red Lead missed the attack. She was out on the prowl and came in after the vicious invasion. She did her usual solicitous meowing at each man in turn as they called for her sympathy.

The victims attended to their injuries and abrasions as best they could for the next hour and would have to wait until the following morning for more serious attention, if they were lucky, from a medico.

No one was in any mood for discussion but Grout insisted on it, and Bolt acquiesced to help focus minds.

'That prick will kill a couple more of us,' Farrow said. 'The officers won't do anything. We've complained about him often enough.'

Some local whiskey was passed around by torchlight as the discussion lapsed.

'The lighthouse fellows told me that he was the main individual in murdering that family, along with Hoto,' Tait said.

'We've looked after Hoto well enough,' Grout said. 'Or at least cholera did.'

'Little Hitler's men shot those lovely girls,' Tait added.

'What do we do?' Farrow asked in frustration. 'What *can* we do?'

There was a further long silence as the throat-challenging alcohol bit hard.

'Should we draw straws on who does what?' Noel asked. He was ignored until Bolt said, 'It must be someone here who really wants to volunteer to . . . do the dirty deed.'

'I once read an Agatha Christie novel, *Murder on the Orient Express*,' Noel said. 'Everyone had a hand in a killing on a train. Everyone had a motive.'

'That was a nice read,' Farrow said, 'but, mate, this is real.'

'I have an idea,' Bolt said.

'Let's hear it,' Bright said.

'No. Just nobody do *anything*.'

'What?' Tait and Grout said in chorus.

'Leave it to me. If you don't know anything, you can't be counted as complicit.'

'Hang on a minute,' Grout said. 'We all just heard you say—'

'I didn't say anything,' Bolt said, opening his hands to the others.

40

A FITTING END

Two nights later, when the entire camp was packed up, ready to march out the following morning, and the men had bedded down, Bolt removed the Colt .45 revolver from the false bottom of his backpack. He sat loading the gun, facing up to what he believed he had to do. This was a different kind of murder. His drowning of the Japanese sailor who tried to kill him in the water was a spontaneous act of self-preservation. This was preservation too, yet it was also premeditated, if he succeeded. He, and all in his group, knew it was only a matter of time before Little Hitler and his thugs struck again.

They had been even more intimidatory since the corporal had not been charged with anything after Wallis's demise. In the four days since the shooting there had been more random bashings of Bolt's group and other POWs.

'It has to stop,' Bolt whispered to a sleeping Red Lead. He patted her, placed one bullet in the gun and crept out into the night.

*

At about 10 p.m. Little Hitler went to the square in search of prostitutes, but all doors, huts and stalls were closed to him and his cohorts. They fired their rifles into the air, but the locals remained shut away. Little Hitler and his men broke into the cottage he had visited earlier in the week. It was deserted. They broke glasses and artefacts, and smashed a mirror. There was not much to loot.

They returned to their truck and passed around beer, which they'd bought from a small Japanese brewery that had been set up a few miles away. It wasn't the best and it had not been chilled but the corporal and his small team of cronies didn't care. If they couldn't have sex, they'd have alcohol and get drunk.

After two hours, they drove back to the camp. An inebriated Little Hitler called for a halt near the latrines. He wanted to take a piss. The corporal jumped unsteadily from the vehicle before it was stopped. He twisted his ankle and was angry. He limped around to the driver's window and pointed a gun at the driver, who cowered back in the seat. Little Hitler tried to fire the gun, but it jammed. The driver, at the urgings of the others in the truck, backed up with a screech and sped off, leaving the corporal standing alone, fuming. He attempted to fire his weapon again. This time it went off. He had trouble putting it back into his belt holster.

Swearing to himself, he began to fumble his penis out.

*

Bolt had watched this violent charade, illuminated by the truck's lights, from behind a tree 30 yards away. Just as the corporal had finished, Bolt crept up behind him and hooked his arm around the man's throat, pushing a knee into his back. Little Hitler, his big frame slack from too much alcohol consumption, was in no state to fight back. Bolt gave one powerful jerk and twist. There was an audible *crack* as two vertebrae in the corporal's neck were broken. Bolt did not let go for another minute, throttling Little Hitler. When the Japanese soldier was on his back and unconscious, Bolt struck him on the throat karate-style, killing him.

Bolt caught his breath then dragged the heavy, limp body to the latrine. With a grunt and several shoves, he pushed it into the 'shit pit'. Only then did he become aware of the awful stench from it, and wafts of the ammonia from urine. He picked up a piece of bamboo, held his breath and probed down with the stick. The body had gone to the bottom in the heavy, foul slop.

Bolt moved away 20 yards, fell to one knee and dry-retched for a minute. He straightened up, walked slowly back to the hot water point and washed thoroughly. At the hut, Red Lead was sitting near the entrance. She meowed and observed him with what he viewed as curiosity. She waited until he was under his blanket and mosquito net and followed him in. He removed his gun from his jacket and placed it in the pack.

Red Lead sniffed around his head and curled close. Bolt lay on his back and could not sleep. He gave a prayer of thanks as his brain went over and over the murder.

During the night, he thought about what would happen next. There would be a search for Little Hitler, probably before midday when the POWs would have been marched out. At least, that was what he assumed. Then he dwelt on the gun in his pack. It worried him until dawn, when he got up and buried it near a clump of bamboo trees.

To everyone's surprise, the march out was delayed. After breakfast, the POWs were ordered to wait in their huts until further notice. Bolt became worried. He could see about 100 Japanese guards scouring the camp area.

'What's that about?' Farrow asked.

'A lost guard, perhaps,' Bolt said, placing a wooden saucer of water in front of Red Lead.

'Really?'

'Why not? They've had a few go AWOL, never to return.'

'Yeah, that's right. Two disappeared at the cholera camp, and I don't mean they died.'

'I believe they've had a few vamoose at every camp,' Bolt said, pulling a face. 'I mean, they're not prisoners, but anyone could go stark-raving nuts out here.'

There were nods of understanding all round.

'The Koreans are the most unhappy working under such conditions,' Farrow said. 'They are almost slaves like us. Just above us on the food chain. The Japanese officers bash their guards, and they bash the bloody Koreans.'

'And everyone bashes us,' Grout proffered.

'Dan,' Bright said, 'you were out for quite a long time last night, weren't you?'

'Yes,' he said with a chuckle, 'I was taking a very big shit.'

*

After an hour, the hut was visited by the three guards who usually accompanied Little Hitler. They ordered everyone out of the hut at gunpoint. Bolt popped Red Lead into the pack and carried her out. The guards searched everywhere, then stalked off to the next hut.

'They were Little Hitler's thugs that had a crack at us the other night,' Farrow said, touching a bandage. 'They don't seem so cocky without him.'

'Where's he, then?' Grout asked.

'Maybe he's gone missing,' Farrow said hopefully.

'I doubt it,' Bolt said, 'I'm sure he's undeterred.'

Farrow glanced at him.

'What do you mean by "undeterred", sir?' Noel asked.

'Perhaps it has a double meaning.'

PART SIX
BURMA BOUND

41

CAMPS OF THE VERY ILL

'You did Little Hitler in, didn't you?' Bright, on crutches, said to Bolt as they finished an arduous two-day march, reaching the second last stop on the railway at Thanbaya Hospital camp. It was 30 miles into Burma and there were nearly 2000 POWs there suffering from all the main diseases, except cholera. Bolt and his group had taken a vote to go there as a small unit to help out; the alternative was to return with the rest of the POWs by train via Kanchanaburi in Thailand and eventually back to Changi.

The work in the cholera camp had inspired them to make an extra effort, with about 50 other medicos and volunteers, to assist the dying and very ill.

'How's your knee?' Bolt asked.

'C'mon, Dan. You did it. All the lads reckon you shot him. We heard a shot when you were out having a bog, allegedly.'

'I didn't shoot anyone.'

'Noel and I reckon you threw him in the latrine.'

'I promised not to tell. Now, no more questions, Leading Seaman.'

The others knew not to probe further on the rare occasion Bolt addressed them by rank. It was always said tongue-in-cheek, yet still a gentle reminder of his rank.

'We never even knew Little Hitler's real name,' Noel said, absent-mindedly.

Grout, looking directly at Bolt, said, 'Shithead, perhaps?'

*

Bolt was up just before dawn on his jog and taking in Thanbaya, which provided a magnificent landscape in the morning. Mist wreathed the mountains and hills like a huge white crochet blanket. The ubiquitous many shades of green dominated the vegetation, interspersed with the occasional clump of light yellow bamboo and magnificent thick brown teak trees. Night rain had soaked the surrounding woods, giving them a fresh, clean feel. A modest wat (temple), gold-painted and in need of repair, was nearby.

The hospital camp had been agreed to by the Japanese a few months earlier in August 1943 to cater for the large numbers of sick. It would have been ideal for recovery but for one salient fact: there were not enough appropriate drugs for the patients, all suffering badly. Some were dying from malaria, which was now resistant to quinine. Others were falling to beri-beri, which left patients bloated. Then there was the ever-present dysentery, along with grotesque tropical ulcers and a score of other serious ailments.

Despite its natural beauty there was an air of depression about the camp. Unsaid was the gloomy realisation that those who could not be helped would be moved on another 60 miles north to Thanbyuzayat, where they would be expected to die. Bolt was aware that he had a 'calling', albeit a temporary one for the rest of his time in captivity. He and the others in his group volunteered to assist the undermanned staff at Thanbyuzayat in the makeshift 'wards', hastily prepared bamboo huts that could be blown over in a storm. This also relieved him and his men of any heavy labour, which had shifted in emphasis now that the railway was complete. Work on the sleepers and cuttings by the local Burmese seemed more cosmetic. The trains were moving through.

The Japanese experiment to build the train route through a mountainous terrain over 280 miles in 18 months was hailed by them as a wonderful engineering feat. It was at the expense of more than 250,000 dead slaves, and twice that number who would never recover fully, mentally and physically, from the most inhumane of projects.

*

Trucks were provided for the drive to flat, less inspiring Thanbyuzayat after much negotiation by Australian officers. There was still an underlying contempt by the Japanese for those who were taken prisoner, and even more disdain for the sick, who were put on half-rations.

This final rail destination was partly a Japanese war administration area, which had been recently bombed by the slowly encroaching Allied forces. The land had been cleared 18 months earlier by Australian and British POWs.

There was a rail marshalling yard and huts for the hundreds of dying POWs.

Bolt and his group were billeted together and organised by doctors, including Frank Cahill and Bruce Hunt. Bolt was chosen to assist Cahill, whose main job at the camp was the amputation of diseased limbs.

After breakfast each morning, Bolt observed Cahill walking into the bush to pray for guidance on where to saw off the offending arm or leg.

'I'm a devout Catholic,' Cahill told him.

'You're a bloody saint! Do you think the prayer helps?'

'I look at it this way,' Cahill said without a trace of cynicism. 'If the patient lives, even a few more weeks, it works. If he dies, then that is God's will.'

The worst moment for Bolt came one day when he was assisting Cahill in sawing off a leg on a POW who'd been given a local anaesthetic. The chop had to be made at the highest possible point on the green and black limb. The only surgical implement available was an old saw found in a farmhouse. It was slow, hacking work and Cahill had done four others in a busy morning. Sweating, he said to Bolt, 'Take over, will you? This fellow has a bone like iron.'

Bolt took a breath and sliced as hard as he could, with the patient aware, and in pain despite the drug. Slide, pull, slide, pull. He worked on until the leg was off. There was a gush of blood.

'Put pressure on the femoral artery,' Cahill ordered, his words quick, his voice firm.

Bolt and another assistant found the thumping artery at the base of the stomach and pressed hard. Cahill attempted to suture the cut.

The patient put his head up.

'Am I gunna die, Doc?' he said, his voice shaking.

'I think so,' Cahill said calmly and softly.

The patient began reciting the Lord's Prayer, with Cahill and Bolt joining in as they worked.

After another twenty minutes, in which the blood stopped running and the patient fell unconscious, Cahill said to Bolt, 'You did well, as you did at Cholera Hill.'

Bolt bowed his head and glanced at the patient.

'Don't worry about him,' Cahill said. 'He's in God's hands. We did all we could.' He paused to clean up. 'How many years' vet work did you do?'

'I dropped out a year before completing my course.'

'Will you take it up after the war?'

'Haven't thought about it. Not sure we'll make it.'

'No, but if you do, I'd consider medicine.'

'Medicine?'

'You're a natural. It's a lot to do with temperament and not being afraid to do what has to be done. You qualify on both counts, and also a third. I've seen how you handle that miraculous cat, one of God's true angel creatures. You have compassion. It helps in medical practice.'

42

A SNAKE TOO FAR

There was a disturbance in the early hours of morning on their fifth day at the terminal camp. Red Lead screamed and howled. There was a thump. Bolt rushed outside with a torch to see her, back arched and on tiptoe as she circled a brown-blotched snake about 5 feet in length. It struck out at her and slithered off into darkness.

Bolt went to pick up Red Lead, but she hissed at him.

'I'd say she's been bitten,' he said. 'Olly, get some boiled water. Brighty, prepare a tourniquet. Your belt will do.'

He grabbed Red Lead by the back of the neck. She wriggled and clawed at him.

'Get me a razorblade, Noel, quick.'

'It was a brown Burmese python,' Noel said. 'Only a small one, but still deadly.'

'I don't care. Get me a blade, now! Here, Grouty, help me pin down the little bitch! She's gone crazy!'

Grout grabbed her two front legs. Bright held her two back legs. Bolt pulled her fur back and found the bite mark halfway up one of her legs.

'Put the belt there,' Bolt said, pointing to the top of the leg. 'Pull it tight. Don't worry if she screams. That's good.'

Bolt made an incision around the bite mark, sucked the wound and spat out the poison. He then swizzled hot water in his mouth and spat again. He repeated this five times. Then he tied a string around Red Lead's neck, and fixed the other end to a tent pole.

'You are grounded, girl, grounded!' Bolt said.

The cat was wide-eyed and furious at the injustice of the rough treatment. She struggled to stand and fell over. The men were stunned.

'Don't you dare die on us now!' Grout said, a tremor in his voice.

'I think I got some of the poison out at least,' Bolt said, using a torch to examine the brown and crimson small puddles where he had spat. He gargled more hot water several times.

'You okay?' Farrow asked. 'You look pale.'

'Mouth's a bit numb.'

'It was a brown python,' Noel repeated. 'They can kill a man by asphyxiation. That one was a junior, but still a thick bugger. Eaten a lot.' He looked at Bolt. 'They can also kill by poisoning, although not as fast or often as the king cobra.'

'You'd better see Frank Cahill right away,' Grout said.

Bolt was on his knees patting Red Lead, who had settled and was lying stretched out and drowsy.

*

'I'll inject this into the bloodstream of both of you,' Cahill said, examining the limp but not lifeless Red Lead in his hut. It was 2 a.m. and the doctor was still up writing a report by candlelight. 'Just to be safe, though, you should both also take this orally. It's an effective Burmese extract from a plant. Force a small amount down her throat.' Cahill injected a teaspoonful in a syringe into the cat's stomach. She hardly winced. He gave Bolt a bigger dose with a quick jab in the derrière, and a further tablespoonful to be swallowed.

'How long before we know?' Bolt asked.

'You'll be fine. This is just a precaution for you. You'd be dead by now if you'd swallowed too much venom.' Cahill patted Red Lead. 'Her situation is more problematic. Best to pray for her soul. My priest back in Melbourne doesn't believe animals have souls; I do.'

*

Bolt was fatigued for the next two days and was able to rest up in the hospital himself. Red Lead, however, deteriorated. She became more listless. She would not eat her food or even lap water. The men took it in turns to monitor her and spoonfeed her water, which meant opening her jaws and tipping the liquid down her throat. The word spread through the camp that the heroine of HMAS *Perth*, Captain Waller's cat, was close to breathing her last. The story of her making it ashore at Java, her heroics as the finest rat-killer of all felines, and her valiant efforts to attack a king cobra and confront a tiger had made her a legend in her short lifetime of three years. Yet it was her gregarious nature, sweet personality and strength of character that endeared her to all and transcended her bravery.

'If there were VCs for cats,' Farrow said, 'she'd get one.'

'Forget the cat category,' Grout suggested, 'she deserves one, full stop.'

Many well-wishers filed to the men's hut to pay their respects. Even one digger, who was almost certain never to leave this death camp, was carried on a stretcher to her side.

She was put on a saline drip. In the week after that she showed signs of a recovery, just as Bolt himself became listless. He had flu-like symptoms: chills in the heat of the day, aches, sweating and headaches.

Cahill examined him. 'It's not the python venom,' he assured Bolt, 'you've got malaria.'

'Damn! I was supposed to be going back to Thailand in a few days.'

'No way you or the cat can make that trip. You'll have to wait at least another fortnight here. I'll quarantine you together.'

Bolt's condition worsened to nausea, vomiting and diarrhoea. Cahill did blood tests. Bolt was found to have anaemia and jaundice. The men were shocked. Here was the fittest individual of the POW community on his back and looking to be at death's door.

*

Bolt insisted that the rest of his group should leave on the train without him.

'I'll only be a short time after you,' he told them, struggling to breathe. 'Besides, I have to wait until Red Lead recovers.'

The men were emotional as they said goodbye to man and cat. Grout and Farrow cried. Tait tried to control himself but ended up blubbering more than anyone. Bright choked on his farewells, but Noel remained stoic.

They sat in silence at Bolt's bedside.

'I wish you'd all buck up,' Bolt said, trying to keep his voice strong. 'We'll see you in a couple of weeks, for godsakes!'

But a pessimistic doctor's report on him and Red Lead had them thinking otherwise.

'The cat won't make it,' Cahill told them without Bolt knowing, 'and Dan, tough as he is, has a pretty bad case.'

43

THE CAT WOMAN
OF MAE SOT

'You're going to Mae Sot on the Burma border with Thailand,' Cahill told Bolt three weeks later in his hospital bed, 'not Kanchanaburi. 'And congratulations, you're a doctor.'

Bolt was perplexed.

'It's the only way I can get you out of this hellhole alive,' he said. 'Everyone who can't walk from here to the railway with their bags will be left to die. Nip Command orders.'

'Mae Sot? How?'

'By truck. The Nips are using Burmese and Thai slaves at Mae Sot for a project, building a bridge or a viaduct, not sure which. You'll be their medico, if you're up to it.'

'You're telling them I'm a qualified doctor?'

'Why not? You're almost a vet. You know all the diseases and drugs needed for the POWs and these workers. I can tell you, no doctors back in Australia would have our expertise in treating tropical diseases. You were outstanding in the cholera camp. You've assisted me on plenty of amputations.

The Nip officers won't know you're not fully qualified. They just want to know you're an *Australian* doctor. They don't trust their own, mainly because none of them understand the tropical diseases and how to treat them.'

Bewildered, but accepting the situation, Bolt asked, 'What about Red Lead?'

'She's half dead, isn't she? Better leave her here.'

'No way.'

'Okay, take her with you. You'll have your own truck and driver. The Nip officers will look after you like royalty. Well, not quite. But they want you alive for medical protection. They're all shit-scared of catching something.'

'How long will I be in Mae Sot?'

'I'm told about a month for the construction.'

'And after that?'

'They'll pop you on a boat to Singapore and Changi, or maybe Japan. Up to them.'

*

The truck ride to Mae Sot was about 500 miles and took three days. On the trip, Bolt had bouts of malarial fever, although he kept it quiet from the Japanese by staying mostly in the truck with Red Lead. He was able to handfeed her all the way with meat leftovers, her favourite pumpkin, and water. By day two she was able to stand, fall over, stand again and stretch. On day three he let her out for a pit stop when the three-truck convoy stopped at roadside stalls. Red Lead was very thin and weak, but Bolt could see she was fighting to survive.

Two Japanese officers came to see him. One had an ulcer on his forearm.

'Piece of cake,' Bolt told him, thinking of the dinner-plate sized ulcer he had removed at Cholera Hill. The officer looked querulous. 'I'll operate in the truck.'

He removed the 2-inch diameter ulcer and bandaged it, asking why the officer had not had it removed on the railway. The officer pretended not to understand. Bolt guessed he didn't trust his own medicos, or he was just plain scared. The ulcer was ugly and the officer may have feared he would die, not an uncommon feeling on the railway.

Mae Sot is a town on the Moei River at the border between Thailand and Burma. Burmese refugees had been flooding into the area and forming camps in 'no man's land', a wooded area on the river between the two countries, which the Japanese had sealed off with heavily armed checkpoints. The Japanese acknowledged the area's ancient Thai name—Wang Takhian—meaning 'water and big trees'.

The Burmese had been running from the Japanese, who were rounding up slaves for their construction work. Yet there was nowhere for the refugees to go. The Thais didn't want them and, under Japanese direction, had prevented them from moving far into Thailand. They had pushed them back into Wang Takhian and over the river into Burma. Now the Japanese were bribing the Burmese men with pitiful wages into labour work along the river.

Bolt's lodgings were in an empty shack in Wang Takhian, a mile from the main town area. The village was a small grid with a few beautifully constructed teak houses seemingly out of place in such an impoverished area. It triggered his memory about what he was told when he'd first met Red Lead. Anna, the young waitress at the Hawkesbury River restaurant, said her father had transported teak from Mae Sot via boat from

Bangkok to Sydney. Anna had mentioned 'the cat woman of Mae Sot', but Bolt couldn't recall her name.

He was driven to a small bridge being built over the river only about 3 miles from the town centre, in Thailand.

An officer told him he would have a hut there for 'worker-accidents'. He wasn't told *if* there were accidents. They were expected. His hours were 7 a.m. to 7 p.m. with an hour's break for lunch and he was informed he was on call 24 hours. A driver would take him to and from the construction site. Bolt insisted on taking Red Lead with him. She was at last showing signs of real recovery, four weeks after the python bite.

Three days into his stay, he began to think more of the so-called 'cat woman of Mae Sot', who had bred Red Lead. He made inquiries in the main town area but no one in the few shops and stores knew her. Then one evening when he was buying food from the only café, really the front room of a hut on the river, he asked the corpulent owner if she knew anybody with a house full of cats. He used paper to draw a house overrun by cats. The café owner and her sister giggled, frowned, gabbled away in Thai for a minute, and finally pointed to the area in which he was staying. They then drew a rough map, showing a temple on the outskirts of the grid, and a laneway.

'Her name Usa,' the owner said. '*Sam sip maew!*' she added, telling him that the woman had thirty cats.

A week later Bolt had his driver take him and Red Lead to the location and was surprised to realise it was less than half a mile from where he was staying. Bolt asked the Japanese driver to wait and opened the front gate of a two-level home. It was an old-style, traditional, well-built

Thai home supported by big, dark-brown teak pillars and topped with a blue-coloured slate roof. The number of cats roaming the small front garden, which featured a small Buddhist shrine with food offerings, indicated he'd come to the correct place. Bolt looked up at the protruding roof gables that ensured tropical rain did not sweep onto the elevated verandah. He slid across a wide, heavy door and entered the compound.

He was about to walk up the steps, when a strikingly pretty woman of about 25 came to the door. She had long black hair, big eyes set well apart and large, sensual lips.

'Can I help you?' she said with a wide, yet guarded smile. She was followed by a tsunami of cats of all shapes, sizes and breeds.

'I'm looking for Usa,' he said.

'I am Usa,' she said with another, even broader smile.

Bolt was tongue-tied. He had expected a totally different vision: an old, large woman in a long dress. Usa wore a shirt of leopard-skin colouring and short fitted pants that showed her thin, shapely legs. She wore no shoes as she gracefully moved down the steps to shake his hand. Ten cats followed and paid very little attention to the new arrival.

Bolt fumbled an explanation of why he was there. She stared at him, taking in every word.

'I remember that man,' she said. 'He did a lot of business with my father and bought four kittens to take to Sydney. He cut teak from forest in Burma and took to Australia.'

'That's right! May I say your English is very good.'

Usa laughed gaily.

'I worked for a doctor and vet—a married couple—in Bangkok. The man was English; his wife French. I picked up the languages from them. They go back to Europe before the war there. Also, my father made me learn English.'

Bolt remembered Red Lead in the truck. He brought her into the front garden and explained about her and how she was recovering from a snakebite.

'I remember her colour, her ... her coat,' Usa said, cradling the cat. 'Poor darling!'

Usa invited him upstairs for a cup of tea in the main entrance room. He admired a large portrait of moustachioed King Rama V, in full military outfit, a pith helmet close by.

'You like him?' she asked. 'My favourite king. He abolish slavery in nineteenth century. He stop Thailand from being European colony.'

Bolt was taken aback by the smell of cat urine, but said nothing. Two copper-coloured roof fans at least kept the main entrance room cool, while not dispersing the odour. Usa put Red Lead down. She tried to look steady on her feet as several cats moved around her in loud silence, feline-style. A concerned Bolt retrieved her.

'She has many brother and sister here,' Usa laughed. She pointed to a large brown and yellow cat looking majestic sitting on a cushion, perched on a teak chaise longue on the verandah at the entrance. 'That is mother, Nuarn!'

'Wow! What a well-fed beauty!' Bolt said. 'Will they recognise each other?'

'Possible. She have twenty kittens, about ten here, all your pussy's relatives!'

Bolt took Red Lead to her mother and sat them next to each other. The mother cat remained lying and propped against a cushion. She gave her daughter a perfunctory sniff and looked away.

304

Red Lead seemed overwhelmed. She jumped to the floor, the first time she'd shown such life since the python bite. The other cats milled around. Some brushed against Red Lead. Others would glide past pretending to ignore her but still getting a sense of the newcomer.

Usa took Bolt to the back area, where there was a cattery the size of a granny flat. Cubbyholes of various sizes were built into the walls, which could each house a cat. There were some in them, others were lounging under a revolving roof fan.

There were two cat flaps.

'They mostly sleep here at night,' Usa said.

'You don't lock them in?'

'No need. The compound is safe. They can wander around at night if they wish. If they want to climb the walls outside, they are welcome. A few have been adventurous enough to enter the scrub and jungle down to the river. One never came back.' She laughed. 'I think that frighten them all!'

'Some sleep with you?'

'Not on my bed. On cushions in the room.'

'Do you feel safe yourself?'

'Come, I show you,' she said.

They returned to the upstairs area facing the door and entered a study. She showed him a samurai sword sitting on a wooden stand. Usa took two revolvers from a desk drawer.

'These are my husband's,' she said. 'He taught me to use them. I have another next to my bed at night.'

Bolt and Usa sat opposite each other at an ornate teak table heavy in appearance but lighter in colour than the other furniture. She asked about his situation. He explained he was a POW, acting as a medico for workers on the nearby bridge.

'And after that is complete?'

'Not sure,' Bolt said, his eyes down. 'It will either be Changi in Singapore, or Japan. It is up to the Japanese.'

'I detest them,' she said, the first flash of anger from her that he had seen. It was another dimension to her stunning appearance, which remained alluring.

'The military officers would rape me like they do others in the village. But Father is very senior in Thai Government. They don't want trouble.'

'Some are bad, some are not.' He changed the subject, keen to learn a little more about her. 'Why do you choose this . . . this wilderness to live?'

'My husband came from Tak, the province. We both preferred bush life, the isolation.'

They watched Red Lead, who was gaining confidence.

'She is certainly uplifted by this experience,' he said.

'I hope not *too* much,' she said. 'Cats can be promiscuous. I think too much excitement might kill her.'

'They wouldn't . . . they're siblings!'

'Cats don't care!' Usa said with a dark expression and a flick of her hair. 'They are incestuous!'

'I didn't know that,' Bolt said, surprised at the information and her directness in conveying it.

The Japanese driver, rifle over his shoulder, rapped on the front door. He tapped his watch.

'Speedo, speedo!' he said.

Usa looked as if she would abuse him. Bolt indicated she should say nothing.

'You can leave Red Lead here, if you wish,' she said. 'Don't take her to the bridge. It's too hot.'

Bolt hesitated. Red Lead was at ease wandering around.

'Come back for her tomorrow, say at this time?'

*

Usa carried Red Lead to the front gate, held her paw and made out as if she was waving goodbye. Bolt felt a pang of guilt. He had been the cat's carer, but she looked comfortable already in Usa's home. He thought again of Red Lead's incredible courage and independence. He felt she would be fine in such wonderful feline company.

44

RECUPERATION

Bolt was elevated by the experience of meeting such a vibrant, strong Thai woman. There was something about her, which he bizarrely compared to Red Lead. They were both attractive, and good communicators. For the first time since being 'dumped' by his fiancée he felt liberated, at least to dream. After almost two years in captivity, Usa was a breath of reality, normality and an inspiration. She was also a vision of hope. His feelings of attraction to a woman, long submerged, had been revived.

He returned the next day as requested, with a different driver. Usa wore a long blue and turquoise dress, into which her figure fitted snugly. She had her hair pinned back. Red Lead approached him from amidst a sea of siblings as he took tea. She had some of her old swagger. She jumped on the chair next to him and meowed, touching his arm with a paw.

'How did she do?' Bolt asked Usa.

'She had fight with one of the boys. He start it, she was too weak to finish it. I push them away from each other. Apart from that, she fine, very relax, very comfortable. It is cat heaven, paradise for her!'

'She slept well?'

'Oh, yes. Longer than her mother. But that is expected after what happen to her.'

He put Red Lead on his lap and stroked her.

'You married?' Usa asked.

'No. I was engaged but I have been away too long. She married someone else.'

'Sorry.'

'Thank you. I'm over it. And you? You mentioned your husband . . .'

'I was married to Thai captain in army.' Her expression tightened. 'He was killed by Japanese fighting in north.'

'I'm sorry.'

'I hate them,' she said with vehemence. She fought back tears.

Bolt leaned forward. He could see his guard sitting under a tree, smoking. He touched Usa's forearm.

'I think the Allies will defeat them,' he said. 'The Japanese are becoming more nervous.'

*

Bolt, under the watchful eye of a guard, returned every day to see Usa and Red Lead. When the bridge was nearly completed, they discussed Red Lead's future.

'You can leave her here,' Usa said. 'I look after her until the war ends. You cannot tell what the Japanese will do.'

'If they send me to Japan, I could not take her . . .'

'No, never! A Thai cat there, not good!'

'I'll have to think about it.'

'This is her real home, remember?' Usa said with a smile.

*

Bolt wandered around the Moei River market one evening, and bargained away his gold watch to a dealer for 300 American dollars, knowing that it was worth at least twice that.

The day before he was to be taken to Bangkok, he made a decision.

'I can't be sure of the future for Red Lead or me,' he told Usa, despondently. 'I would appreciate you taking her.'

Usa kissed him on the cheek.

'You are a good man. I will take very good care of her. Promise. But she is no trouble. She's stronger now. She picked out boy who attack on second day. She beat him up! After that I think she is queen of the pack. Her mother does not mind.'

'I have money for you to—'

Usa shook her head and smiled.

'I have thirty-three of them. She makes thirty-four. I have money from my father. It's not a problem.'

He pressed 200 dollars into her hand.

'Please accept it. I have some for Singapore, where they are sending me.'

Usa kissed him on the mouth, which surprised him.

Bolt cradled Red Lead in his arms, stroking her and chatting to her. She was content. She then purred and curled up on an armchair. Bolt cried lightly, wiped away tears and took the moment to leave. He hugged Usa.

'I shall do everything I can to come back for her,' he said, locking eyes with Usa, 'and you.'

Usa began crying. She smiled warmly through the tears and said, 'I want you to.'

*

Bolt had just bedded down on his floor mat in his one-room shack at 10 p.m. when he heard a light knock at the door. It was Usa. She embraced him. Without a word, they fell onto his bed and made passionate love through the night.

PART SEVEN
BACK TO THE PAST

45

UNOFFICIAL DEGREE
FROM CHANGI

Bolt joined fellow POWs at Changi in February 1944 and wrote every week to Usa, but without response. He suspected she was not receiving his letters. He had tried to let her know that they had made the correct decision not to take Red Lead with him. Rats had become a major problem at Changi and at first he regretted not having her there, where she would have been effective in countering the infestation. Seventy-five cats were introduced into the prison but within two months they had all disappeared. The food was so poor and scarce in Changi that the cats were being caught and eaten.

Bolt was in recovery from malaria, and was still having bouts of extreme fatigue but they were becoming fewer. It saw him in hospital a couple of times but soon he was a permanent fixture there at the request of Cahill and Dunlop in dealing with the illnesses suffered by a majority of the inmates. They had him doing every possible medical job and treated him like a fellow doctor. He became intrigued with all aspects of medicine, including psychiatry, which was under the direction of Major (Dr) John Cade. Before the war Cade had been a senior psychiatric specialist in Melbourne. During his Changi years he witnessed firsthand how mental health was affected by chemical imbalances in the brain, and nutrition.

Cade showed Bolt how to experiment with certain foods to see if they had an impact on the minds of the hundreds of patients they had to deal with.

After a month of tests, they examined the results.

'What does that tell you about one particular nutritional group?' Cade asked him.

'Blind Freddie could answer that,' Bolt said. 'The worst cases of mental illness lack plain old salt.'

'Correct. After the war I am going to specialise in the development of lithium, a naturally occurring salt, in the treatment of psychiatric disorders such as manic depression.' He waved a hand at the room full of patients. 'All of this lot have got varying degrees of these medical issues.'

'So the old diagnoses of "madness" and "lunatic" are . . .'

'Largely primitive, like burning witches at the stake. I want to change all that.' Cade paused and added, 'As for your remark about Blind Freddie, there are a lot of eye problems in here. They're not getting enough carrots and oranges for a start.'

'Luxuries!'

'Non-existent in Changi.'

*

In September and October 1944 the Japanese officers and guards at the prison began to show signs of strain. They were tetchier, even more likely to deliver bashings, and never relaxed.

On breaks from the hospital, Bolt would gaze up and notice more activity in the skies. Small Japanese planes were using the nearest aerodrome with greater frequency. Air-raid sirens and drills came more often. Blackouts were common. There was a ban of all sports, music, entertainment and community singing. Gatherings of more than six of any kind were stopped. Bolt often ran around the prisoner camp perimeter with Peter Chitty, winner of the unofficial Changi Brownlow for the Australian Rules competition in the prison in 1942, and four others. Guards stopped them and would only allow them to jog two at a time.

A telltale sign that the Japanese feared attacks, even invasion, was that the guards now wore tin hats at all times. Armistice Day—11 November—brought the greatest joy to the entire POW camp to that point. Forty US B-17 four-engine bombers rumbled overhead. Air alarms sounded. Guards ran for cover while POWs stood, cheered and waved. Bolt and other medicos heard the crushing, thunder-like sound and ran outside to see the massive planes pass low over the camp, and then climb high to avoid Japanese fighters.

Guards yelled admonition from safe places. When the bombers were out of sight and only their diminishing *boom* could be heard, the guards came out waving rifles, forcing men to cower and go back to their appointed jobs. The planes returned the next day, and became a daily event, much to the joy of the POWs.

'They're flying too high to be challenged by any Jap planes,' Bolt said to Cade one morning in the hospital.

'The Japs don't even bother to take off,' Cade said.

'It's an indicator. The Americans are closing in.'

Japanese officers began to step up the digging and deepening of trenches. They feared invasion. Bolt joined hospital staff to mark out a big red cross close to the building, hoping this would mean it avoided attacks. The act increased consternation among the Japanese, who were now paranoid about the Allies coming at them from the air, land and sea.

On 8 January 1945, their fears seemed less irrational when at 1 p.m. a US air raid of B-29 Superfortress bombers loomed over Singapore and unloaded on the Seletar naval base on the north-east coast in full view of the POWs. They were awesome flying machines, the biggest ever built. Prisoners with radios were able to report that 4000 were pouring out of American production lines. At the risk of bashings, POWs began to chide the guards with the figures, implying that the end of Japanese rule in the region was nigh.

*

By early 1945, Bolt had still not heard from Usa. They had only known each other for a month, but he had begun to fantasise about her. He wondered if this was irrational, and if his mind was slipping a little. Yet every time he pictured her in his mind, he felt she was perfect for him, even his soulmate. Bolt tried to compare the feelings he had for his former fiancée with those he now had for Usa. He even scribbled a list of characteristics, such as intelligence, empathy, warmth, personality, beauty and sex appeal. Usa was preferred on all counts. It made him both nostalgic and depressed. A year had slipped by since that idealised brief time with her.

Usa's love for pets and cats was another comparison in which she came out on top. Pamela hated cats. He admitted to himself that his thoughts were a little lopsided after a bare four weeks with the stunning Thai, and nearly two years with the Australian. He knew also that one night of glorious sex, a night of feverish passion, was not a realistic way to judge compatibility. Yet it had been *real*.

*

In February 1945, Bolt received letters from his group—Tait, Grout, Farrow, Bright and Noel. They had been shipped to Japan to work as slaves in coalmines. He was delighted to learn they were all still alive, despite a run of illnesses. There was hope in their letters, which had to be guarded and cautious to pass the Japanese censors on small cards, with little room for real expression.

Then in August 1945, everything changed. The Americans dropped two atomic bombs on Japanese cities and forced them to surrender. Bolt considered going back to Mae Sot to see Usa and Red Lead but he would have been AWOL. The POWs were not yet freed. That took another two months. Leaving before official repatriation and demobilisation would have had repercussions.

In October, Bolt and the emaciated contingent of Changi POWs were freed and shipped home. For most it was a grand moment to see family and friends. Bolt had no close family alive, and no woman to meet him at Spencer Street train station when he arrived there mid-October. It heightened his determination to see Usa and Red Lead again.

*

This seemed an impossible dream by late 1945. He had no money and there were no boats to Asia straight after the war. He contemplated becoming a sailor on anything that would get him to Bangkok. But he'd had no word at all from Usa and the dream of her began to fade.

Bolt started to think more practically about his life and career. He decided on becoming a qualified doctor. Armed with letters of recommendation from Cahill, Dunlop and Cade, he applied to do the shortened Melbourne University medical course offered to a select few straight after the war. His credits in vet science helped. He was allowed to start in year three of a six-year course that had been truncated for the privileged few to just five years.

He worked as a freelance medical correspondent for Australian papers and magazines from 1946 to the end of 1948 when he finished his basic medical degree. This work gave him a modest income on which to survive while boarding in a one-room Carlton flat close to the medical faculty. Bolt had plans to specialise in tropical medicine or psychiatry, or both. But first there were Usa and Red Lead to consider.

In late 1948, he wrote to her again, and finally, after not having had any communication from her for five years, he received a letter, which explained she had never received any from him. She had sent plenty to him, she noted. Usa spent a page describing Red Lead, which brought Bolt to tears. She was now seven years old, in very good condition, and the best friend to her mother Nuarn, who was ailing at fifteen.

Bolt was due to receive his degree in March 1949, but could not wait for that, and instead arranged for a friend to pick it up on his behalf. He worked hard on all his naval contacts and finally wangled a berth on an army ship heading to Southeast Asia for an unspecified (secret) mission to do with fighting communists on the Korean peninsula.

Bangkok would be a major stop.

46

AN UNEXPECTED REUNION

Dan Bolt hired a Norton motorbike and rode the 300 miles to Mae Sot in hot but good weather just before New Year 1949. He parked the bike outside Usa's Wang Takhian home, where a few cats roamed the front garden. Usa, who heard the roar of the bike, came hurrying down the steps holding Red Lead. There was a three-way hug that caused the cat to jump clear. She meowed her approval and sat a few yards away as Usa and Bolt embraced. He produced an emerald engagement ring and asked her to marry him. She was embarrassed.

'No need to rush things,' Usa said, 'until you know everything.' She turned and looked up to the front door. 'Achara,' she called and beckoned a little girl to come down the steps.

'This is my daughter,' Usa said. 'Do you like her?'

A lovely child of about four years bounced down the steps, smiling and giggling.

Bolt was stunned.

'Do you like her?' Usa repeated.

'Is she . . .'

'Buy one get one free,' Usa said with a mysterious smile.

'She looks . . .'

'Mixed Thai and European.'

'Well, yes, she is lovely! What a smile!'

'My dear,' Usa said to the child, 'shake hands with Doctor Bolt. He is your father!'

The child held her hands at chest height and bowed.

'*Doctor* Bolt,' Usa said, 'meet your daughter, Achara.'

He was stunned.

'It means "pretty angel",' Usa said.

'You never said anything in the letters.'

'No. I didn't want you or her to know unless you came back, for good.'

Bolt was speechless.

'And do not ask me if she is really yours!' she said, wagging a mock finger at him. 'I have not had sex since that night with you. She looks more European . . .'

'Australian!' Bolt said, reeling happily from the surprise.

'Pardon me, Doctor. But our family is waiting for her Thai looks to emerge.'

He took the child by the hand and walked up the steps into the house. Nuarn, the mother cat, was lolling on a cushion on the chaise longue, as she always had. She opened her mouth and made a squeak when he patted her. Bolt looked down into the garden to see Red Lead waddling at her own pace to the steps and up. He noticed a new photo-portrait of the bespectacled young Rama IX, who'd taken the Thai throne aged nineteen in 1946. It was hung alongside Rama V.

Bolt sat with Red Lead next to the mother cat and cuddled and patted her. Red Lead nuzzled her face into Bolt's cheek, sniffing him.

'She's checking it's me,' he said.

'Oh, she knows it's you. I have been telling her for weeks you were coming.'

Red Lead began to purr. She caressed and massaged his chest.

'You accept all this—the cats, Red Lead, a ready-made child, me?' Usa asked.

'Yes, more than ever!' he said.

'Then I shall answer your question.'

'What?'

'Yes, I shall marry you, *Doctor*!'

*

Later that day, after a passionate reunion with the door shut to all the cats, including Red Lead, Usa remarked, 'You look like film star.'

'Who, me?' he said. 'You mean Johnny Weissmuller?'

'You are a little like him, but no.'

'You mean a Thai film star?'

'No, American. Robert Mitchum. You have his hair, his chin . . .'

'Oh, yes, the cleft chin, the dimple. The proboscis, the ears . . .'

'The eyes.'

'Oh, really? He looks permanently hungover.'

'Warm! I also like Quirk Dougus.'

'Quirk? Oh, you mean Kirk Douglas?'

'Yes.' Usa laughed.

'How do you know of them?'
'We see many American movies since the war.'

*

They discussed their future. Bolt said he would get qualified as a medico in Thailand.

'We will move to a bigger city,' Usa said. 'For you to practise, and our daughter's education.'

'Any preference?'

'Chiang Mai. My family has settled there.'

47

OF EMPATHY,
COURAGE AND LOVE

Bolt, Usa, Achara, Red Lead and the other cats settled in
Chiang Mai. It was Thailand's second biggest city but still,
in the 1950s, predominantly rural and both he and Usa
preferred it to Bangkok. They rented for a few years then
bought a two-storey, colonial-style building on the River
Ping in the south-east of the city. It had five bedrooms and
sizeable back and front gardens. Bolt had a 25-yard pool
built in the backyard and swam every day he was in Chiang
Mai. He rented medical offices and opened a practice
there on the canal near the city's Thapae Gate, a 2-mile
motorbike ride from his home. He had two surgeries, the
second one being for veterinary work. He soon gained
a strong reputation for handling humans and animals,
and no one ever queried his lack of official documenta-
tion as a vet. He kept up his interest in psychiatry and
tropical diseases, and gained postgraduate status in both
in Thailand.

He stayed in contact with people in Melbourne, mainly through his vast medical interests, and visited his former home once every two years, usually at Christmas and into January when it was quiet.

Each member of Bolt's group of POWs made the pilgrimage, some with wives, to Chiang Mai to see Bolt and Red Lead. They stayed in the roomy mansion. At first, they had been reluctant to return to the country of the slave railway, and the memories of daily misery and inhumanity that went with it. Bolt reminded them that Red Lead, while hale and hearty at age fifteen in 1956, could not have long to live, if the average lifespan for a cat was considered.

'She is fortunate to have a most sympathetic medical carer close by most of the time,' Bolt wrote to Grout. 'He can only do so much to keep her kicking, although I must say, she is the fittest animal or human of her years, age equivalent, I have ever attended or seen. I know she would enjoy very much seeing her "team" again.'

That was enough incentive for Grout, who broke the drought and made the trip at Christmas 1956. Then each year after that Tait, Noel, Farrow and Bright followed.

In 1961 Edgar Burroughs came with his wife, Michelle, and Bolt and Usa visited them in Chicago in 1962.

All the men made a huge fuss of Red Lead, whose gregarious, warm personality masked whether or not she really knew who they were. Whatever her true feelings, she was close to them all when they left her home. All, including Noel, were in tears on parting.

Bolt told Usa, 'Red Lead represents hope, and love and courage, which they all had to show during those terrible years.'

On 10 October 1965, Red Lead, as usual of her own volition, joined Bolt in the pool for a swim in the early morning. She had her favourite breakfast of fish and pumpkin and went to sleep in a shaded outdoor hammock in the afternoon, as she often did. She did not wake up. It was a shock for Bolt, who had always admired her agility and control over all her faculties right to the end. It was just about the time of her 24th birthday, a very old age for a cat. He cried, but in his sadness reflected on her incredible life.

Bolt buried her in the back garden of their home, where she had lived for most of her life. He had a bronze cross made. He inscribed on the attached plaque:

RED LEAD 1941–1965
MASCOT OF HMAS *PERTH*
A CAT OF EXCEPTIONAL CHARACTER

He, Achara and Usa, who favoured Red Lead above all the scores of cats she'd ever had, were sad for weeks. He wrote to the Australian Department of the Navy recommending that Red Lead should be remembered in some way. Bolt also wrote to all the men, who replied with heartfelt letters. Noel had the most telling lines of all.

'I now understand what empathy really means, having studied my condition since the war,' he said. 'That small animal gave me an inkling of what real love and emotion are. In my mind, she has not passed on. She lives in my thoughts forever.'

Bolt had the letter copied, framed and hung in the guest-room of his house.

*

Dan Bolt died of a heart attack in 1982, just after his 77th birthday. He was still running his Chiang Mai medical practices, part-time, until the day before he died. Bolt left a comprehensive private autobiography, which he said was never to be published. In it he confessed to the murder of two Japanese men, one a sailor in the water on a Java beach, and another an army corporal in the POW camp at Three Pagodas Pass, Thailand.

He and Usa were happily married for 32 years. She passed on five years later, aged 68. Their one child, Achara, died in 1996, aged 52, after a motorbike accident, surrounded by her 30 cats. Her breeding business was bought by a Chiang Mai local, who put the feline parade on show daily for cat-loving tourists.

The third ship to be named HMAS *Perth* has Red Lead's red paw prints on the companionway leading to the bridge. There is also a painting of Red Lead on the bridge. The wardroom door has a cat flap that reinforces the memory of this remarkable feline. These features on *Perth* III, the last of eight ANZAC Class frigates, are in honour of Red Lead and to keep alive the memory of the gallant ship, the outstanding Captain Waller, and his courageous crew.

ACKNOWLEDGEMENTS

The Red Lead story had been relayed, superficially through the decades, by sailors, and she had 'appeared' in many books and articles. I had known of this cat saga for more than 65 years. It was first told to me by a Melbourne sailor and dentist, Bill Chalmers.

In 1979 and 1980, I carried out research for a fiction work set in Indonesia, *Blood is a Stranger*, and doubled up with Red Lead in mind, visiting certain locations, including the Sunda Strait and the Javanese coast. More recently I did reconnaissance and research in Indonesia again, as well as Singapore, Thailand, Burma, Australia, the UK and France.

I was delighted when Allen & Unwin publisher Tom Gilliatt asked if I had a story on a cat. Two previous books by me on animals at war, *Bill the Bastard* and *Horrie the War Dog*, had been successful, and I wasn't surprised by the request.

I had three other books on animals in mind: one was on an elephant in north Thailand.

Another publisher several years earlier asked if I had any more animal stories. I mentioned the elephant.

'Is it an Australian elephant?' I was asked.

'No.'

The publisher lost interest.

The other two true narratives were on cats at war. One was about Ooboo who had a cameo in *Horrie*. The other story was of Red Lead, which was set in Southeast Asia. I was a fraction more intrigued with the latter.

My thanks to the families of the key characters—the sailors of HMAS *Perth* and other prisoners of the Japanese in World War II. They were guarded because of the experiences of their relatives, but still more than helpful in explaining the sailors' circumstances. Some told anecdotes; others provided solid information, including private unpublished diaries.

Many thanks to Tom Gilliatt for backing the book and copyeditor Deonie Fiford.

Roland Perry
March 2020

BIBLIOGRAPHY

Agar, Augustus, *Footprints in the Sea*, Evans, London, 1959.

Aspinall, George and Bowden, Tim, *Changi Photographer: George Aspinall's Record of Captivity*, ABC Enterprises and William Collins, Sydney, 1984.

Bergamini, David, *Japan's Imperial Conspiracy*, William Heinemann, London, 1971.

Braddon, Russell, *The Naked Island*, Werner Laurie, London, 1954.

Carlton, Mike, *Cruiser: The Life and Loss of* HMAS *Perth and Her Crew*, William Heinemann, Sydney, 2011.

Caulfield, Michael, *War Behind the Wire*, Hachette Australia, Sydney, 2008.

Coates, Albert and Rosenthal, Newman, *The Albert Coates Story*, Hyland House, Melbourne, 1977.

Cody, Les, *Ghosts in Khaki*, Hesperian Press, Perth, 1997.

Courtney, Bryce, *Matthew Flinders' Cat*, Viking, Sydney, 2003.

De Laroche, Robert and Labat, Jean-Michel, Aurum Press, London, 1993.

Dunlop, E.E., *The War Diaries of Weary Dunlop*, Nelson, Melbourne, 1986.

Frame, Tom, *Pacific Partners: A History of Australian-American Naval Relations*, Hodder & Stoughton, Sydney, 1992.

Galaxy, Jackson, *Cat Daddy*, Penguin, London, 2013.

Grenfell, Captain Russell, *Main Fleet to Singapore*, Faber, London, 1951.

Hall, Leslie, *The Blue Haze*, Kangaroo Press, Sydney, 1996.

Johnson, Carl, *Carrying On Under Fire and Captivity*, History House, Melbourne, 2009.

Kinvig, Clifford, *River Kwai Railway*, Brassey's, London, 1992.

Lindsay, Patrick, *The Spirit of the Digger*, Pan Macmillan, Sydney, 2003.

Macdougall, A.K., *Collins of the* Sydney, Clarion Editions, Sydney, 2018.

Mery, Fernand, *The Life, History and Magic of THE CAT*, Grosser and Dunlop, New York, 1975.

Nelson, Hank, *Prisoners of War*, ABC Enterprises, Sydney, 1985.

Parkin, Ray, *Ray Parkin's Wartime Trilogy*, Melbourne University Press, Melbourne, 1999.

Payne, Alan, HMAS *Perth*, Naval Historical Society, Sydney, 1978.

Perry, Roland, *The Changi Brownlow*, Hachette Australia, Sydney, 2010.

Ramsay, Ian, *POW*, Macmillan Australia, Sydney, 1985.

Richards, Rowley, *A Doctor's War*, HarperCollins, Sydney, 2002.

Savage, Russell, *A Guest of the Emperor*, Boolerong Press, Brisbane, 2004.

Schultz, Duane, *The Last Battle Station*, St Martin's Press, New York, 1985.

Rivett, Rohan, *Behind Bamboo*, Angus & Robertson, Sydney, 1948.

Thomas, David, *Battle of the Java Sea*, Andre Deutsch, UK, 1968.

Van Der Post, Laurens, *The Admiral's Baby*, William Morrow & Co. New York, 1997.

Warner, Dennis and Peggy, *Disaster in the Pacific*, Allen & Unwin, Sydney, 1992.

Wilson, Keith, *You'll Never Get off the Island*, Allen & Unwin, Australia, 1989.

Wigmore, Lionel, *The Japanese Thrust: Australia in the War of 1939-45*, Volume IV, AWM, Canberra, 1957.